Making Connections
Science 7

Making Connections

Authors

Ted Anderson
Head of Science/Biology
East York Collegiate
Toronto, Ontario

Art Geddis
Head of Physics
East York Collegiate
Toronto, Ontario

Rick Wahrer
Head of Physics
Newtonbrook Secondary School
Willowdale, Ontario

Science 7

General Editors
Gerry Connelly
Vice-Principal
Regina Pacis Secondary School
Downsview, Ontario

Ken Stief
Co-ordinator of Science
North York Board of Education
North York, Ontario

Senior Consultant
Dr. Graham Orpwood
Consultant, Science and Education
Toronto, Ontario

gage EDUCATIONAL PUBLISHING COMPANY
A DIVISION OF CANADA PUBLISHING CORPORATION
TORONTO ONTARIO CANADA

Copyright © Gage Educational Publishing Company, 1988
A division of Canada Publishing Corporation
Toronto Ontario Canada

Written, printed, and bound in Canada

Communications Branch, Consumer and Corporate Affairs Canada has granted
permission for the use of the National Symbol for Metric ⚡ Conversion.

Canadian Cataloguing in Publication Data
Anderson, Ted, 1941-

    Making connections: Science 7

For use in schools.
Includes index.
ISBN 0-7715-3000-5

1. Science. I. Geddis, Arthur N. (Arthur Norman), 1941-
II. Wahrer, Rick, 1946-   . III. Title.
Q161.2.A52 1988   500   C87-093242-X

1 2 3 4 5 6 AP 93 92 91 90 89 88

Cover Art and Book Design: Peter Maher/NewtonFrank
Illustration: Jon McKee, Jock MacRae and Peter van Gulik
Photo Editor: Susan A. Cox
Typesetting: Trigraph Inc.

Acknowledgements

Gage Educational Publishing Company gratefully acknowledges the assistance of the following teachers in developing the *Making Connections: Science* series:

Ken Ashcroft
Young Offenders' School
Hamilton, Ontario

John Eix
Upper Canada College
Toronto, Ontario

Joni Heard
West Lynde School
Whitby, Ontario

Nancy McGregor
Joseph Gould Sr.
Public School
Uxbridge, Ontario

Gerry White
Bayside Jr. High School
Saint John, New Brunswick

Cyril Davis
St. Raymond's School
Toronto, Ontario

Michael Halley
Forest Glen School
Moncton, New Brunswick

Robert Howitt
Wallace Public School
Gowanstown, Ontario

Anne Ross
Saint Mildred's
Lightbourn School
Oakville, Ontario

Barbara Worth
St. Raymond's School
Toronto, Ontario

Douglas Davis
Beaverbrook School
Moncton, New Brunswick

Chester Hannay
Bath Intermediate
Bath, New Brunswick

Elizabeth Hoyt
George Street Jr.
High School
Fredericton, New Brunswick

Vincent Tassone
St. Boniface School
Scarborough, Ontario

Contents

Introduction

The title of this book, *Making Connections*, is what science and education are all about. The study of science helps you to understand many things about the world around you and to make connections between your personal experiences and the global environment.

Scientists, along with specialists in many other fields, look at the world and try to make sense of what they see. They do this by developing ideas that help them to make connections or find explanations for the things that they observe. For example, an artist looks at the world and reproduces it for others by controlling light, shade, and texture. By contrast, historians use time to make connections between events. They look at what led up to and what followed the events that they want to understand.

Scientists also try to understand the world but they develop different ideas and use different methods to make connections between phenomena. Using this book, you will learn how some of their ideas help to make connections among things in your world. In addition, you will learn how to use scientific ways of investigating phenomena and how to test these connections by observing, hypothesizing, and experimenting.

This book is also about making connections between science, technology, and society. The cover of the book shows a running shoe and the first chapter will help you to understand how the practical problems of designing good running shoes are connected with the science of materials. The technology that society depends on for everyday life usually is based on scientific discoveries and ideas.

Finally, education is about making connections too. Throughout your life you will learn more and more about how to connect with other people and with other people's ideas. Science education in school is part of that process. As you learn about science, you are making connections with the world of science and technology. And in today's environment, when so much in our lives is affected by changes in science and technology, that is a pretty important world with which to make connections.

Graham Orpwood

Making Connections
Science 7

1

Properties of Matter

Have you ever run across gravel in your bare feet? If so, you know how useful running shoes can be. They give you a good grip on the ground and protect your ankle and knee joints by cushioning each impact. They also must allow your feet to flex freely. Shoe manufacturers know that these features are important to any runner. You probably do too, even if you choose your shoes just because you like the color.

Modern running shoes are made from a number of different materials. Each of these has a special purpose. The shoe manufacturer must decide which materials to use for each purpose. For example, which material will provide the most comfort? the most traction? the most strength?

In this chapter, you will explore ways to solve these sorts of problems. You will learn that all objects are made up of some form of material or **matter**. Matter always takes up space and always has **mass**. In a running shoe, you want the matter to have as little mass but as much strength as possible. Through the use of **technology**, running shoes with both of these features can be made. Technology is the application of science to solve a certain problem such as the design and manufacture of running shoes.

1.1

Materials for a Running Shoe

For specialized jobs like the production of the running shoe, technologists first need to select different kinds of matter, or materials. To make this selection, they have to understand the characteristics of different materials. Which materials can provide the strength, lightness, and flexibility necessary in a running shoe?

This problem will be the focus of this chapter. Like a running shoe technologist, you will be trying to find solutions to practical problems involving running shoes. Practical problem solving can be approached in a systematic way, as represented by the **problem-solving model** on page 5.

An artificial heart is made from very special materials.

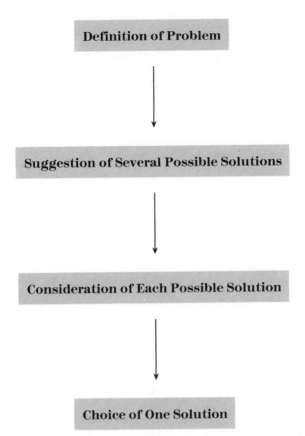

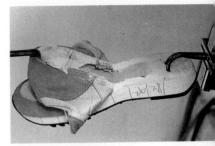

Special machines are used to test running shoe materials.

Definition of Problem

↓

Suggestion of Several Possible Solutions

↓

Consideration of Each Possible Solution

↓

Choice of One Solution

A good way to begin the suggestion of possible solutions is to study materials that might be useful. In order to understand the characteristics, or **physical properties** of any kind of matter, technologists must do careful tests and make observations. Only then can the material confidently be used in technology.

Describing Properties of an Object

Modern running shoe technology is based on a scientific knowledge of properties of matter. This knowledge is combined with design ideas that use the matter effectively. In this activity, you will observe and describe the properties of a running shoe. In order to observe, you must use one or more of your five senses: sight, hearing, smell, taste, and touch.

ACTIVITY 1

Materials

running shoe
metric ruler

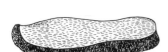

Exploded Diagram of a Running Shoe

Procedure

1. Locate the major parts on your shoe.

   outsole   toe
   insole   upper shell
   heel   laces

2. Observe each part, list its materials, and list its properties, such as shape, color, and flexibility. Use whichever senses best help you to observe.

3. Write a brief description of each property. Here is an example.

Part of Shoe: Outsole		
Materials	**Properties**	**Description**
rubber	shape	like a foot

Discussion

1. Discuss and compare your results with your classmates. If your discussion gives you any new ideas for properties of the shoe, add them to your description.

2. What types of materials were used to make the running shoe? Which of these materials did you identify directly by observation? Which materials did you have to guess at, based upon your observations?

3. Some of the running shoe's features were created by its designers. Others are properties of the materials used. Which of your observations are design features?

4. Pick some of the design features used and explain why they are important for the shoe.

Extension

1. What are some differences among shoes used for different activities, such as work boots and track shoes?

2. Research and compare the structure of shoes used in different activities.

Measuring Properties

In the previous activity, you used your senses to describe the properties of a running shoe. But your senses alone can only give you a limited amount of information. For example, can you tell the mass of a running shoe just by holding it in your hand? For measuring properties like mass, our senses need some help.

What is mass? It is a measure of the amount of matter in a given object. The basic unit used for this measure is the **kilogram**. The symbol for kilogram is **kg**. This measure is unchanging. For example, an object with a mass of 1 kg on the earth would also have a mass of 1 kg on the moon. The term you commonly use for mass is **weight**. The weight of a 1-kg object on the moon is different from its weight on the earth. For most purposes, on the earth you can consider mass and weight as the same thing.

ACTIVITY 2

Using a Balance

The mass of an object is often an important design feature. Lightness is generally an advantage in running-shoe design. It is difficult to judge a shoe's mass from its appearance, or its feel on your foot. You can use the balance to extend your senses, and measure an object's mass.

In this activity you will first estimate an object's mass by using your senses. You will then use a balance to measure the mass of an object in metric units.

Materials

two different types of running shoes
triple beam balance

Procedure

1. Hold one shoe in each hand and predict which is heavier.
2. Estimate each shoe's mass in kilograms.
3. Check your estimates by using a balance. Follow these steps to find each shoe's mass.

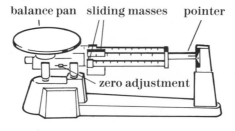

balance pan   sliding masses   pointer

zero adjustment

Step 1
Make the balance level. To do so, adjust the levelling feet until the bubble is centred in the level indicator.

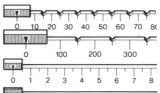

Step 2
Slide all masses to zero on each beam.

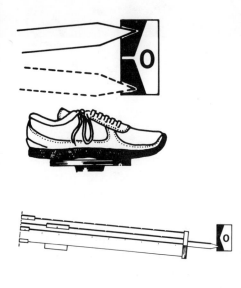

Step 3
Turn the zero adjustment on the balance until the beam swings equally above and below the zero point.

Step 4
Place the shoe on the balance pan.

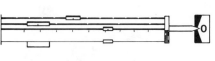

Step 5
Slide the largest mass along the beam, one notch at a time. Keep doing so until the pointer at the end of the beam tilts down. Then slide the mass back one notch.

Step 6
Repeat step 5 with the second largest mass.

Step 7
Slide the smallest mass to the right until the pointer balances at the zero point.

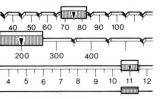

Step 8
Determine the mass by adding the readings on each beam.

4. Record the masses.

Discussion

1. Do you think running shoes have generally been getting heavier or lighter in recent years? Why?

Extension

1. Practise estimating the masses of several objects in the classroom. Use the balance to check your estimates. Obtain two objects of approximately the same size such as two books. Hold one in each hand and see if you can tell which is heavier. Then put them on a balance and determine each of their masses in grams. How did the quantitative measurement of mass differ from your estimate?

Matter Matters Everywhere

Matter does not exist everywhere in the universe. In fact, most of the universe is empty. But matter has important effects, even in places where there is no matter at all. For example, large bodies like the sun are capable of bending light, which usually travels in a perfectly straight line. When the Viking spacecraft visited Mars, the planet was on one side of the sun while the earth was on the other. Scientists noticed that they could receive Viking's radio signals, even though the sun should have blocked them. The signals were *bending* around the sun.

This bending was caused by the sun's huge gravity. All bodies generate gravity, but only large ones create a noticeable amount. The more matter a body contains, that is, the more mass it has, the more gravity it generates. Many scientists have inferred that the solar system came about when a huge cloud of gas and dust began to fall together from its own gravity. Gravity attracted the smaller particles to the larger bodies, eventually making the planets and the sun.

Gravity is extremely important for life on Earth. It helps to hold water in the seas, where many scientists think life on Earth first arose. Gravity also makes it possible for the earth to have a thick atmosphere, unlike such bodies as the moon.

Simulating a situation without gravity allows things (and people) to float around.

The gravity of the moon is too weak for it to have a thick atmosphere like the earth has.

For these reasons, scientists think that life may be very unlikely on small planets with little gravity.

The sun is a star, one of countless millions in the universe. The sun and the other stars bathe the universe in light and other forms of radiant energy. They are able to do this because of the huge quantities of matter they contain. The staggering gravity they generate produces great pressure and heat inside them. This pressure and heat causes nuclear burning to take place, which generates light. Sunlight is, as you know, vital to life on Earth. Do you think life could exist on other planets receiving light from other stars?

Volcanic eruptions are caused by the great heat and pressure inside the earth.

Connections

1.2

Knowing: Observations and Inferences

You can find out about the world by direct use of your senses. When you do this you are making **observations**. You touched and looked at the outsole of the running shoe, and observed its color and texture. If you tried to bend it, you observed that it was flexible.

At the same time, you made **inferences** about what you observed. Making an inference involves using your previous knowledge to form an idea about your observations. You probably suggested that the running shoe was used for running. However, it might well have been used for walking or jumping. It might even have been used to cover the foot of a mannequin in a store window.

There is always some uncertainty in an inference. If you are aware that you are making an inference, you can make further observations to decrease this uncertainty. Without further observations, you may make a serious mistake.

You can use your observations and inferences to predict what will happen. When you do this you are forming a **hypothesis**.

There can even be some degree of uncertainty in apparently simple observations. For example, examine these lines.

Which of the Two Lines Is Longer?

Which of the two lines is longer? Are you sure? Measure them with a ruler to check.

The use of measurement is a good way to decrease the uncertainty of observations. When you measure, you give a number to a property of an object or material. Properties that use numbers to describe an object are called **quantitative properties**. You are probably familiar with quantitative properties such as length, width, and volume. These properties are used to describe objects. You are probably not as familiar with quantitative properties used to describe materials. You can find these properties by quantitative measurement. Some of these will be investigated in the next section.

Questions

1. Steel nails are used to hold pieces of wood together.
   a) What design features of a nail are suited for this function?
   b) What properties of the nail can be changed so that it can hold together pieces of wood of different sizes?
   c) What properties of steel make it a good choice of material for nails? Is steel ever a poor choice of material for nails? Why?
   d) Screws are also used to hold wood together. How do they compare with nails in terms of design features and the materials from which they are constructed? How are the different properties related to the functions of nails and screws?

2. The middle of the sole of a running shoe is often made of a plastic foam which contains millions of tiny gas bubbles. What function does the midsole serve? How do the gas bubbles help this function?

3. What properties would be important in a material to be used for footwear? For each of the following examples of footwear, suggest a property important for its use and a material which has that property.
   a) running shoes
   b) construction boots
   c) snowmobile boots
   d) wading boots
   e) slippers
   f) swim fins

4. You see a clear, colorless liquid in a glass. What could you infer about the liquid? What else might it be? Suggest some other observation that you might make to decrease the uncertainty of your inference. *Note: Smelling or tasting of unknown substances can be dangerous.*

1.3

Describing Materials: Properties of Substances

In order to describe the matter making up an object, you have to ignore design features and pay attention instead to properties of materials or substances. Color is one property of the substances in a running shoe. Some other properties of substances are flexibility, strength, elasticity, conductivity of heat, conductivity of electricity, and flammability. How many other properties of the substances of a running shoe can you name?

Two properties important in life jacket materials are buoyancy and visibility.

ACTIVITY 3

Check Your Grip

An important function of running shoes is to provide good footing under various conditions. In this activity, you will test the gripping characteristics of some types of running-shoe treads. To make this test, you will measure how much you have to pull on the shoe to get it to slide along a surface.

Materials

running shoes with various tread types
calibrated spring scale (or a strong rubber band and a
metric ruler)
brick or other heavy object

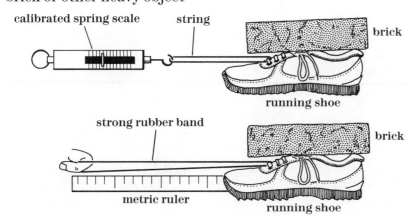

Alternative Set-ups
for Activity 3

Procedure

1. Decide the following conditions for the grip test.
   a) Which shoes are to be tested?
   b) What surface will be used?
   c) How much load will be placed on the shoe each time?
2. Assign a number to each shoe. Record properties which you
   think will affect the shoe's grip.
3. Predict which shoe you believe will grip the best on the
   selected surface. State this prediction in the form of a
   hypothesis. Choose the shoe that you believe will be second
   best, third best, and so on, if you wish.
4. Attach the spring scale or elastic band as shown.
5. Gradually increase the pull on the shoe. Measure the
   extension of the scale or band at the moment when the
   shoe begins to move.
6. Record your results in a table like the one below.

Shoe Number	Test Number	Test Results*	Average Pull*	Rank
	1	4.6		
1			4.5	3
	2	4.4		

*Units depend on those used on the scale. Average pull will be the average
of the two test results. To find the average pull, add the two results and
divide by two.

7. Repeat each test and record your results.
8. Compare your results with your hypothesis.

Discussion

1. How did your results compare with your hypothesis? If there are differences, do you see any reasons for them?
2. How would the load on the shoe have affected its grip? Was the load on the tread in each case exactly the same? Could this have affected the results?
3. What properties of the treads seemed to be most important?
4. Would results have been different on a smoother or a rougher surface? Explain.

Extension

1. Repeat the test, this time choosing different conditions in the first step of the procedure.
2. Check advertisements for car tires. Which ones appear to have the best grip? Under what conditions?

1.4

Fair Tests: Quantitative Properties of Substances

Many of the properties that you are familiar with are **qualitative properties**. When you describe a rock as large, yellow, and hard, you are giving some of its qualitative properties. Scientists, however, sometimes find it helpful to make measurements that can be expressed in numbers. They describe objects in terms of quantitative properties like length, volume, and mass.

An impressive quantity of water flows over Niagara Falls.

When you try to describe quantitative properties for substances, you have to be sure that you measure the material itself, and not the object. Suppose, for example, that you were trying to compare the strengths of wood and steel. Pins are made of steel, and fence posts are often made of wood. Pins and fence posts are objects, while steel and wood are substances. You can probably bend a pin easily, but probably can't bend a fence post at all. This does not mean that wood is stronger than steel. We know that the strength of an object partly depends on its thickness. To have a **fair test** of the strengths of wood and steel, you would have to compare samples of the materials that are the same thickness, for example, a pin and a toothpick.

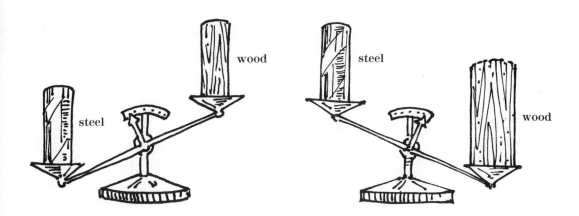

In order to be sure that you are making a useful comparison between two substances, you must devise a fair test. It would not be fair to compare running-shoe treads by testing one on pavement and another on wet grass. To have a fair test, the conditions of the test must be the same.

Observing Compressibility: The Crush Test

ACTIVITY 4

The outer sole of a running shoe must be very durable so that it can take a lot of scraping without being damaged. Between the tread and your foot, however, softer materials are used. These materials absorb some of the shock of your foot's impact with the ground. In a running shoe, the most useful property of these materials is their compressibility.

In this activity, you will attempt a fair test of the compressibility of some common materials. You will compress them using the weight of a brick. The sample of material must be at least 2 cm thick. Materials such as foam rubber, fibreglass insulation, or styrofoam could be tested.

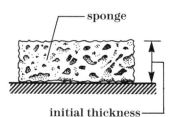

sponge

initial thickness

Materials

brick
metric ruler
several common compressible solids

Procedure

1. Prepare a table like the one below for your observations.

Material	Initial Thickness (cm)	Compressed Thickness (cm)	Compression (cm)	Compressibility
Sponge	3.4	2.6	0.8	$\dfrac{0.8 \text{ cm}}{3.4 \text{ cm}} = 0.24$

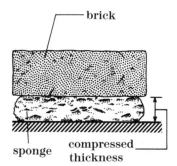

brick

sponge   compressed thickness

2. Set a solid on a flat surface. Measure and record its initial thickness.
3. Place the brick on the solid as shown. Measure and record the compressed thickness.
4. Repeat steps 2 and 3 for each solid.
5. Calculate the amount of compression for each material by subtracting the compressed thickness from the initial thickness.
6. Calculate the compressibility for each material. To do so, divide the compression by the initial thickness.

Discussion

1. Which material tested would be best for use in the design of the insole of a running shoe? Why?
2. Did all of the materials spring back to their initial thickness when the brick was removed? Is this an important property in the design of the insole? Why?

Extension

1. Rank these substances in order of compressibility: rubber, iron, wood, water, and air.
2. What is the maximum possible compression for any material? How could you test this?

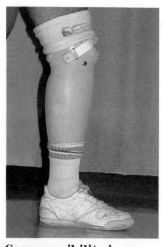

Compressibility is an important property of artificial limbs. It ensures comfort and stability.

Measuring the Strength of Materials

The strength of an object depends on factors other than the material from which it has been made. For example, you could not use polyester thread to lace your running shoes, even though polyester is a strong material. The thread would be too weak, simply because it was not thick enough. In order to have a fair test of the strengths of two materials, you have to ensure that all other factors are the same.

In this activity, you will determine the effect of the length, and then the width, on the strength of a sample of material. In this way, you can test the relative strength of a number of different materials.

Materials

set of equal masses
polyethylene (from a plastic grocery bag)
aluminum foil
paper
adhesive tape

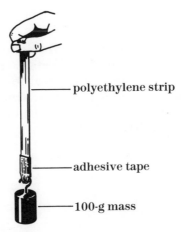

polyethylene strip

adhesive tape

100-g mass

Procedure

1. Cut a strip of polyethylene 7 mm × 70 mm. Use adhesive tape to attach a 100-g mass to the end of the polyethylene strip. Holding the polyethylene strip by the other end, lift the mass.

2. Add a second 100-g mass, and then try to lift the total of 200 g with the polyethylene strip. Continue to add 100-g masses, until the polyethylene strip cannot lift the mass and breaks. Record this mass as the breaking strength of the polyethylene strip.

3. Repeat this procedure with polyethylene strips of the following dimensions: 7 mm × 140 mm, 14 mm × 70 mm, 14 mm × 140 mm.

4. Record your data in a table like the one below.

Material	Dimensions (mm)	Breaking Strength (g)
polyethylene	7 × 70	
polyethylene	14 × 70	

5. Cut equally sized pieces of aluminum foil and paper. Repeat steps 1 through 4 for the aluminum foil and the paper.

Discussion

1. What properties of the strips of material did you make the same? Why did you make them the same?
2. Is the breaking strength of the material affected by its width? by its length?
3. Did any properties seem to not make any difference?
4. Which material was the strongest? Did this surprise you?

1.5

Scientific Knowledge for Technological Solutions

The original meaning of the word science was knowledge. The aim of science is to obtain knowledge about the world. Sometimes science is done to satisfy a natural curiosity about the world. Sometimes science is done to find knowledge about specific problems. This knowledge can be used in technology to solve problems that arise from the needs of society. In the following activity, you will collect information to help you solve a practical problem.

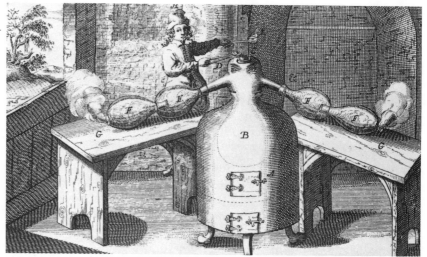

Early chemists heated materials in furnaces to find out about them.

Investigating Properties of Materials

In this activity, you will investigate the properties of some materials that could be used for footwear.

Materials

paper
polyethylene (from a plastic grocery bag)
rubber sheet
aluminum foil
styrofoam
wood
nylon fabric
other materials that might be appropriate

Procedure

1. To determine if the material is waterproof, stretch it over a beaker and pour some water on it.
2. For each of the materials, investigate some other relevant properties. Some possibilities are strength, flexibility, and cushioning ability.
3. For each property investigated, rank the materials. For example, under *Waterproof*, list first the material that is most waterproof, and continue listing until you have noted the least waterproof material.
4. Compare your results with the results of the class.

Discussion

1. Classify the properties investigated by the class as quantitative or qualitative properties. Write them in two separate lists in your notebook under the appropriate heading.
2. The cushioning or shock-absorbing properties of a material are important for the manufacturing of running shoes. So is strength. Name some materials that have both strength and good shock absorption.
3. List any properties of any of your materials that would make them especially suitable or especially unsuitable as footwear material.

In our solar system, extremes of temperature make matter behave strangely. On the scorched surface of Venus, rocks partially melt, and flow slowly downhill. On the other hand, frozen water is abundant in the cold outer reaches of the solar system. This frozen water is so cold that it is harder than some of the hardest rocks on Earth.

Artists' Paints

Acclaimed by art critics as being one of Vermeer's greatest works, *Supper at Emmaus* was actually a forgery by Han van Meegeren.

Then

Han van Meegeren, perhaps the most successful of all art forgers, was put on trial in Holland in 1945 for selling priceless Vermeer paintings to the Nazis. At the time of his death in 1947 he still had not convinced the world that he was the painter of six paintings that art experts considered among Vermeer's greatest work. Finally in 1968, a scientist used a technique related to radiocarbon dating, called radiochemical analysis, to show that the paintings were indeed forgeries.

Van Meegeren was so successful in his forgeries because he took great care to use exactly the same types of materials that were used by master painters of the past.

For centuries, painters made their own paint by mixing ground-up colored substances with egg yolk, gum, or different kinds of oil. The colored substances, called pigments, were usually minerals and colored earth. The most common pigment, lead white, was made by stacking lead in fermenting grape skins or animal dung. The white substance produced on the surface of the lead was used as a pigment.

Although artists had some brilliant colors to choose from, they still had a limited choice. Many of the most brilliant yellow, orange, and red pigments contained substances such as arsenic, mercury, and antimony. Like lead, these substances are poisonous.

Artists also had problems with the oils and egg that were used to bind the pigment. Over long periods of time these substances cracked, darkened, and often provided food for the bacteria and insects that destroy many paintings.

Now

Concerns for convenience, safety, and durability led to welcome changes in artists' paints.

Modern acrylic paints provide a wide range of beautiful colors, as illustrated by this painting. Called *Yellow Church*, it is by Canadian painter David Thauberger.

New pigments were created from substances as they were discovered or purified. Some of these substances are chromium, cobalt, copper, zinc, and titanium. Forgers have often made the mistake of using pigments developed after the date that the painting was supposed to have been completed.

In the late 1800s, many new dyes and pigments were created from petrochemicals. Among the most sensational of these were vivid greens and purples.

Pigments also were mixed with new binders. Paints made with synthetic substances such as acrylics do not seem to darken and cannot be digested by bacteria or insects.

However, there may be problems even with the new paints. Scientists and artists do not yet know how durable these new substances are. Artists experiment with new techniques, sometimes causing paint to crack or flake. Some modern works of art done with certain kinds of inks have disappeared completely, because they fade under display lights.

Artists and scientists are now working together to develop the best materials to use for paintings.

1.6

Technology: Solving Practical Problems

In this chapter, you have been learning how the best materials for running shoes are selected. You have observed some materials and their special properties. Some of these properties, such as strength, are important to the function of an object. Other properties, such as cost or color, are important too, but for reasons other than the object's function.

Technology is used to construct objects that will perform a specific function. To use technology, first you need a clear idea of what the function of the object will be. In other words, you need to know the purpose of the object.

ACTIVITY 7

Selecting Footwear Material

In this activity, you will develop a case for the use of a particular footwear material. You will then present this case to the rest of the class. In doing so, you will attempt to convince your classmates that your material is the best choice.

Materials

wading boot
dress shoe
construction boot
tennis shoe
sandal
bedroom slipper
ballet slipper

Procedure

1. Your teacher will divide the class into groups. Working with the others in your group, consider the examples of footwear and choose one of them.
2. Select a material that you think would be most suitable for the sole of this type of footwear. To do so, use the problem-solving model on page 5.
3. Once your group's material has been selected, consider its various properties. Prepare a case to show how and why this material is best suited for the sole of the footwear you have chosen.
4. Appoint a salesperson from your group to present your case to the rest of the class for the final class decision.
5. Organize your information in a way that will make it easy to present to the rest of the class. Use a large poster, a series of overheads, or some other suitable format. Consider not only the scientific factors, but other ones, such as

cost and attractiveness. Also consider some of the less
desirable properties of your material, so that your salesperson can counter the arguments of the other groups. Present
your information clearly, briefly, and in a way that will
attract the attention of your classmates.

6. Listen carefully to the case presented by the salesperson
   for each group.

7. Once all of the cases have been presented, make a class
   decision on which groups successfully solved the problem.

Discussion

1. For each example of footwear, consider its usefulness for
   walking, running, climbing, and five other uses of your
   choice. Then rate each example of footwear as good, fair, or
   poor for each use.

2. How well were the properties of the various materials presented? How did this affect your observations? Did the salespeople miss any important properties that would have been useful?

3. How effective were the salespeople? Were some good materials rejected because the scientific information was not presented well?

4. What factors other than the scientific ones were important to your decision? Would these factors be important for other groups making decisions?

Questions

1. a) Name five different materials used to make drinking cups.

  b) Which properties would you consider in making a choice of the material for a drinking cup? What factors other than the properties would you consider?

  c) For some situations, you might choose one cup material over all the others. Describe the situation, your choice of material, and the reason for your choice.

2. Over the last few years, more and more plastics have been used in the construction of automobiles. What advantages are there in the use of plastics? What are the disadvantages?

3. Until a few years ago, most grocery stores used paper bags. Today, almost all use polyethylene bags. Compare the advantages of **a)** polyethylene over paper, and **b)** paper over polyethylene as materials for grocery bags.

During World War I (1914-1918), lighter-than-air airships, called zeppelins, were used almost as much as airplanes. These zeppelins were filled with hydrogen, which is the lightest of all gases. Because the zeppelins were filled with hydrogen, they could float on the air, which is heavier than hydrogen. For this purpose, however, hydrogen has a rather serious shortcoming: it is highly flammable. When enemy airplanes fired on a zeppelin, it would catch fire and even explode.

John McLennan and Helium

John McLennan

Early airships like the Graf Zeppelin used hydrogen, which is very flammable.

To make zeppelins safer, a physicist at the University of Toronto named John McLennan suggested that helium might be a good substitute for hydrogen. The British Navy was interested in this odorless, colorless, lighter-than-air gas because of its relative safety. It agreed to sponsor McLennan's research into methods of obtaining helium from natural gas. This research resulted in the development of a method that produced helium for a reasonable cost. McLennan's later work included investigations into a wide variety of topics, including cosmic rays, submarines, and cancer. In 1935, he was knighted for his accomplishments.

In the fifty years since McLennan's research, zeppelins have not provided much competition for airplanes. Since 1979, however, the Hystar Development Corporation of Vancouver has been working on the development of a craft which is a cross between an airship and a helicopter. The craft became known as a Hystar.

The Hystar was developed to make it easier for logging firms to remove logs from remote locations. Helicopters are being used for this task even though they are expensive to operate and have limited load-lifting capacity. The craft developed by George Ninkovich and his team of engineers at Hystar uses a helium-filled envelope. It provides the primary lift, while propeller/rotors provide extra lift and steering.

The Hystar can travel over a range of speeds from 2-100 km/h and is easily steered. As well, its operating costs are about one third those of a helicopter. With these characteristics, the Hystar may well prove useful for other applications such as crop spraying.

The Hystar—a modern, lighter-than-air airship

Summary

Objects are made from different materials, or kinds of matter, to perform different functions.

Materials can have qualitative properties or quantitative properties. Quantitative properties can be measured and scientists sometimes find them more useful.

Inferences (guesses) about an object involve using previous knowledge to go beyond the observations. There is always some uncertainty associated with an inference, which may be reduced by further experimentation and observation. Knowledge can also be used to make inferences and hypotheses.

When comparing the properties of different materials, you must be sure that you use a fair test. A fair test depends only on the materials and not on the design of the objects being compared.

In technology, scientific knowledge and problem-solving models are used to find solutions to practical problems.

Chapter Questions

Remember

1. For each of the following objects, specify a design feature, and a property of the material from which it is made. Then indicate how each of these features and properties is suited to the function of the object.

   a) a spoon
   b) a china bowl
   c) a knife
   d) a paper clip
   e) a woollen mitt
   f) a screwdriver

2. Which items in the list below are substances? Which are objects?

   bottle   notebook
   water   ink
   wood   air
   pen   balloon
   rubber   tree

3. Obtain a drinking cup or similar object.

   a) Determine four qualitative properties of your cup.
   b) Determine four quantitative properties.
   c) Which of the properties you have selected are design properties of the object? Which are properties of the material from which it has been made?

4. Mary is a new girl in your class. You observe that she doesn't talk to any of the other students, seldom smiles, and always has her homework done. Think of two different inferences that you might make about Mary. What might you then do to test these two inferences?

5. a) Which weighs more, a kilogram of styrofoam or a kilogram of steel? Explain your answer.
   b) In science try to use words very carefully. Explain why it doesn't really make sense to say that "styrofoam is lighter than steel."

Precision instruments reduce the uncertainty in measurements. This surveying instrument measures angles very accurately.

Wood has always been a good material for many kinds of sports equipment, but new materials are becoming popular. Aluminum baseball bats and tennis racquets are usually more durable than wooden ones. Hockey sticks are often reinforced with plastic and glass fibres. A strong form of graphite, similar to the lead in your pencil, is becoming popular in tennis racquets and golf clubs.

Think

1. The size of large crowds of people can be estimated by taking an aerial photograph of the crowd, marking it off into a number of squares, counting the number of people in one of the squares, and multiplying this number by the number of squares in the crowd.

   a) What observations and inferences are you using in this method?

   b) What might you do to increase the accuracy of this method?

How many people do you think are in this picture?

2. The use of different materials in the construction of an object may give rise to major changes in its design. Compare the design differences in chairs made from the following materials.

   a) steel

   b) plywood

   c) solid wood

   d) plastic

   e) upholstery

3. Different materials are often combined to balance a weakness that one of them may have. For example, glass fibres are strong but brittle; they are combined with a resin, which protects them from breaking, to make fibreglass. Why do you think the following materials are combined?

   a) reinforced steel rods in concrete

   b) nylon with cotton for gym socks

   c)   plastic foam and rubber for the sole of a running shoe

   d)   nylon mesh and suede for the top of a running shoe

4. Plates can be made of china, plastic, paper, or metal.

   a)   List some of the advantages and disadvantages of using each of these materials.

   b)   Which of these materials would you choose for plates in the following situations? Explain the reasons for your choices.
   - a meal in a restaurant
   - a picnic for 20 people
   - a canoe trip

Dream

1. List some of the properties of suitable footwear material for the following people.

   a)   an Inuit hunter   d)   a marathon runner

   b)   a construction worker e)   a dancer

   c)   an angler   f)   a grade-seven student

2. Numerous new materials are used in deep-sea exploration. What are some of the properties that an ideal material for construction of a mini-submarine would have to have?

3. The soles of running shoes need to be fairly thick so that they can absorb the shock of a runner's foot hitting the ground. Unfortunately, this tends to make them heavier as well. How might you combine two or more materials to produce a sole that was light and still a good shock absorber?

Pisces IV, a mini-submarine used by government and university researchers

Decide

1. Every day you use your shoes for a large number of different activities.

   a)   List some of your activities and the properties of a footwear material necessary for these activities.

   b)   Decide which materials would be best for making your shoes.

2. Roads have been made from many different materials: concrete, asphalt, gravel, and even wood.

   a)   List the advantages and disadvantages of these materials for road construction.

   b)   Decide which material would be most suitable for roads in the situations below. Explain the reasons for your decisions.
   - a city neighborhood
   - a desert
   - the Arctic

Asphalt is a common material used in road construction.

2

Characteristics of Life

In his novel, *The War of the Worlds*, the writer H.G. Wells describes intelligent Martians looking at the earth through a powerful telescope. The Martians watch the earth's inhabitants as if they are "the transient creatures that swarm and multiply in a drop of water." Like Wells's Martians, scientists have looked for life on other planets using many complex instruments. So far, they have found no signs of life.

However, you can use an instrument that reveals a world that *is* filled with life. This instrument, the **microscope**, lets you look into the lives of countless kinds of tiny waterdwellers. By observing them, you can get a better understanding of all forms of life.

Are there characteristics which different forms of life all have? With the microscope, you can begin to answer this question. In this chapter, as you learn to use the microscope, you will study some of the basic characteristics of life. You will be looking at cells, which make up all living things, both plant and animal. Some of the creatures that you will be observing consist of only a single cell, but even so, you will see that they are quite alive.

2.1

Observing Microscopic Life Forms

Anything that is too small to be seen by the unaided eye is called **microscopic**. You might have seen photographs of microscopic plants and animals on television or in books. Now, you are going to observe them for yourself.

ACTIVITY 1

Observing Pond Water

In this activity, you will observe pond water in two different ways.

Materials

150-mL beaker or baby-food jar
magnifying lens
pond water

Procedure

1. Fill the beaker or jar one-quarter full of pond water.
2. Observe the water without using a magnifying lens. Record what you see. Look in particular for anything that appears to be alive.
3. Repeat step 2 using a magnifying lens.

Discussion

1. Compare your observations made with the magnifying lens to those made without a magnifying lens.
2. Did your observations from step 3 reveal any additional signs of life?
3. What evidence is there that some of what you observed is alive?

Structure of the Light Microscope

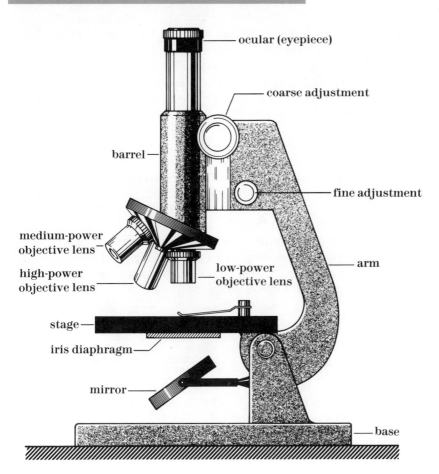

The Light Microscope

ocular (eyepiece)

coarse adjustment

barrel

fine adjustment

medium-power objective lens

high-power objective lens

low-power objective lens

arm

stage

iris diaphragm

mirror

base

If one magnifying lens makes an object appear larger, then two magnifying lenses, one on top of the other, may make the object appear larger still. This is the basic idea used in the construction of a microscope. The two lenses are found at opposite ends of a hollow, metal cylinder called the **barrel**. The barrel is attached to a metal piece called the **arm**. The top lens, which you look through, is called the eyepiece or the **ocular**. The lens at the lower end of the barrel is called the **objective lens**. You may have a microscope with more than one objective lens. Each objective lens is a different length. The shortest objective lens is the low-power lens, and the longest objective lens is the high-power lens.

The arm is attached to a heavy piece of metal called the **base**. Attached to the arm are usually two pairs of round knobs, one pair larger than the other. The larger knobs are called the **coarse adjustment**, and the smaller knobs are called the **fine adjustment**. When you turn the coarse adjustment, the barrel moves up or down (depending on which direction you turn the knob), and you will see this movement. When you turn the fine adjustment, the barrel will again move up or down. This movement is so small, however, that you cannot see it.

The flat structure supported by the arm is the **stage**. The stage has a round hole in its centre. The object to be viewed is placed on top of the stage, over the hole.

Under the stage, you should find a movable mirror or a built-in electric light. If not, you will need a portable source of light. The purpose of the mirror or the electric light is to direct light up through the hole in the stage. Attached directly underneath the stage is a circular piece of metal with a hole in its centre. The size of the hole can be made larger or smaller. This part of the microscope is called the **iris diaphragm**. It controls the amount of light that passes upward through the hole in the stage.

As you can see in the picture of the microscope, there is more than one objective lens at the bottom end of the barrel. You can change an objective lens by simply turning the lenses until another objective lens is directly under the barrel. When an objective lens is in its proper position under the barrel, you will notice that it clicks into place.

Questions

1. The base of the microscope is rather heavy. Suggest why this is so.
2. When you turn the coarse and fine adjustment knobs, what part of the microscope moves?
3. What is the advantage of having more than one objective lens?

4. Why is the object to be viewed placed directly over the hole in the stage?

Care and Use of the Light Microscope

When you carry your microscope from the storage area to your desk, you should place one hand around the arm and the other under the base.

You may have a microscope that has more than one objective lens. Each objective lens is a different length. The low-power objective lens should be over the hole in the stage when you store your microscope.

To clean the eyepiece and the objective lens, you should use a piece of special paper called **lens paper**. *Do not clean the lenses with any other material except lens paper*. Lens paper is specially made so that it will not scratch the lenses.

Using the Microscope

ACTIVITY 2

In this activity, you will practice using the microscope. The object you will observe is called the **specimen**. The first specimen that you will look at is a hair from your head.

Materials

microscope with light or mirror
slide
lens paper

Procedure

Part A: Getting Ready
1. Set up the microscope and review all the parts.
2. Carefully pluck a single hair from your scalp.
3. Place the hair on the middle of the slide.
4. Place the slide on the stage of the microscope so that the specimen on the slide is over the hole in the stage.
5. Set the low-power objective lens in place directly under the barrel.

Part B: Adjusting the Microscope

In order to observe the specimen clearly, it is very important to learn how to focus the microscope and how to adjust the light.

1. If your microscope has a light source under the stage, plug the light into a wall socket and turn the light on. If your microscope does not have a light, use a mirror. Adjust the mirror in this way.

   a) Look through the eyepiece of your microscope.

   b) At the same time, adjust the mirror so that it points toward a source of light, such as a window.

   c) Keep on adjusting the mirror until the circle of light you see in the microscope is as bright as you can get it.

2. In order to focus the microscope, look at the microscope from the side. As you do this, turn the coarse adjustment *very slowly* so that the microscope barrel moves down toward the stage.

3. Position the low-power objective lens close to the slide. *Be careful that the low-power objective lens does not touch the slide.* If the objective lens touches the slide, the lens might get scratched. Some microscopes are made so that the barrel will stop before the objective lens touches the slide. However, not all microscopes are made this way, so position the objective lens carefully.

4. Now that the objective lens is close to the slide, look through the eyepiece again. As you do this, slowly turn the coarse adjustment *in the opposite direction*, so that the barrel moves upward.

5. Notice that the specimen becomes clearer as it comes into focus. Once the specimen is in focus, turn the fine adjustment until you see the specimen as clearly as possible.

6. In your notebook, sketch what you see. Write a brief description of the hair, noting characteristics such as color and texture. Write as if you were describing the specimen to a friend over the telephone.

7. After you have completed your sketch and description, observe the specimen under the medium-power objective lens. In other words, use a more powerful lens to further enlarge what you are seeing. Do this in the following way.

   a) Move the medium-power objective lens under the barrel. *Do not touch either the coarse or fine adjustment knobs as you do this.* You will notice a click when the objective lens is in place.

   b) Sharpen the focus by slowly turning the fine adjustment. You should not have to touch the coarse adjustment at all.

   c) Note any additional observations you can now make.

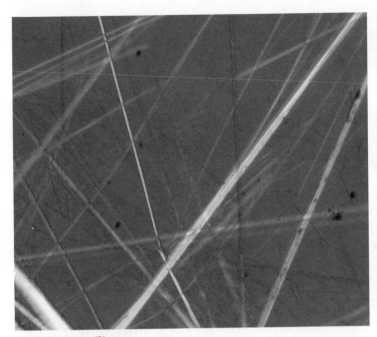

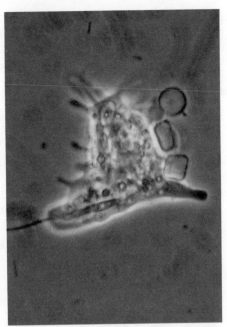

a) Asbestos fibres

b) An aquatic organism, a protist

c) Crystals of vitamin C

Microscopic views of various materials

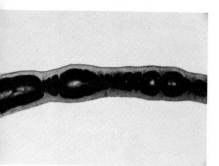

Microscopic view of a strand of hair

8. Turn back to the low-power objective lens again. Get a strand of hair from one of your classmates with a hair color different from yours. Place this strand across the one already on the slide.

9. Observe both strands of hair under the low-power lens and medium-power objective lens. Describe any difference that you see in the two strands of hair.

Discussion

1. Compare your observations made under the two different powers. Comment on how hairs of different color and texture appear under the microscope.

2. Which way did the hair appear to move as you moved the slide from right to left? up and down?

ACTIVITY 3

Using the Microscope to Observe Pond Water

In this activity, you will observe pond water under a microscope and describe your observations.

Materials

microscope with light or mirror
slide
lens paper
pond water
eyedropper

Procedure

1. Set up the microscope and review all the parts.

2. Using an eyedropper, place one drop of pond water in the centre of a clean slide. Place the slide on the stage of the microscope. Make sure that the specimen on the slide is over the hole in the stage.

3. Using the low-power objective lens, observe the drop of water under the microscope. Write a description of what you see.

4. Using the medium-power objective lens, observe the drop of water. Make a note of what you see.

Discussion

1. Compare your observations with those you made using a magnifying lens. Did the microscope reveal anything to you that the simple magnifying lens did not reveal?
2. If you did see other things, were any of them alive? How do you know?

Perhaps you said that some of the objects you saw in the pond water were alive because they were moving. You see many things that move. For example, you have seen bicycles, cars, waves, and television images move. Are these things alive? On the other hand, when you see a dog running, a bird flying, or a person walking, you think that because of their movement, these things are alive. What is the difference between these groups?

Through the study of pond water, you can get an idea of how scientists recognize that certain things are living and others are not. The microscope can be used to help identify characteristics of living things.

2.2

Recognizing Life

Are lichens alive?

Observing *Elodea*

In this activity, you will observe common water plants called *Elodea*. *Elodea* grow in ponds and lakes and are also common aquarium plants.

Materials

microscope
slide and coverslip
lens paper
Elodea
eyedropper

ACTIVITY 4

An aquarium plant

Procedure

1. Using an eyedropper, take water from a jar containing *Elodea*. Place two drops on the centre of a clean slide.
2. Gently remove one small leaf close to the top of the plant. Place it in the water on the slide.
3. Place one edge of the coverslip on the slide so that the coverslip just touches the water.

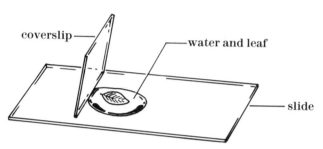

4. Using a pencil, *slowly* lower the other end of the coverslip until it lies flat on the water. This prevents air bubbles from forming under the coverslip. The coverslip flattens out the water so that the high-power objective lens cannot touch the water.

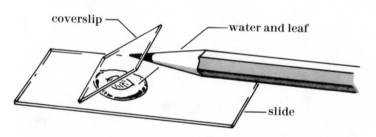

5. Place the slide on the stage of your microscope with the specimen over the hole in the stage. Make sure that the stage is level. If it is tilted, then water on the slide will escape and the specimen will dry out.
6. Remembering how you focussed the microscope before, observe the specimen under low power. If you want a particular part of the specimen in the centre, move the slide.
7. Now view the specimen under the medium-power objective lens. Try to avoid using the coarse adjustment knob. The fine adjustment knob should allow you to get the specimen in focus.
8. You will see structures that look like bricks in a brick wall. Look for small green circles within these structures.
9. Once you have found the small green circles, look at them in a number of the structures and see if any of them are moving. Draw one of the structures.

Movement in Living Things

Each brick-like structure in the specimen of *Elodea* you observed in Activity 4 is called a **cell**. The small green circles within it are called **chloroplastids**. You may have noticed some of the chloroplastids moving.

One of the ways in which scientists determine if something is alive is to look for **movement**. Movement is a characteristic of life. Living things move in order to get food, to avoid danger, or in some cases, to find a mate.

Without the use of a microscope, you could not see the movement of some of the things in pond water. Nor could you see the chloroplastids in the *Elodea* cells.

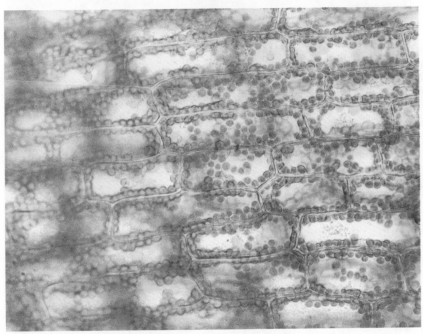

Microscopic view of cells in the *Elodea* plant

Observing *Euglena*

ACTIVITY 5

In this activity, you are going to look at another type of living thing found in pond water called *Euglena*.

Materials

slide and coverslip
lens paper
Euglena
eyedropper

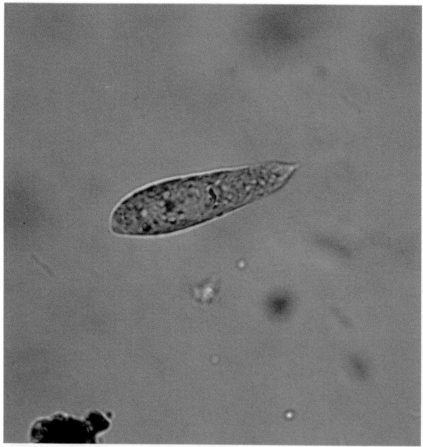

Microscopic view of an *Euglena* cell

Procedure

1. With an eyedropper, take water from a jar or beaker containing *Euglena*. Place two drops on the centre of a clean slide.
2. Repeat steps 3, 4, and 5 from Activity 4.
3. Observe the specimen under the low-power objective lens. Locate one *Euglena* cell. Look at the illustration above to help you identify it. Move the slide so that the *Euglena* cell is in the centre.

Discussion

1. Does movement of the chloroplastids mean that the chloroplastids are alive, or that the cells containing them are alive, or, that both are alive?
2. Are the *Euglena* you are observing alive? How do you know? Without the microscope, you might not even suspect that the water contained living things.

Irritability in Living Things

When you examined *Elodea* and *Euglena* under the microscope, you observed movement.

Movement is usually the most noticeable characteristic of life. However, there are other characteristics that all living things share.

Living things **react** to changes in their environment. The capacity of living things to react to changes is called **irritability**.

Think about your own body. If the air around you gets cold, you might begin to shiver. Shivering helps to keep you warm. Shivering is an example of irritability. If you are doing strenuous exercise, your body gets warm. How does your body react when you become too warm?

You can look for irritability in other living things.

The Dutch scientist Anton van Leeuwenhoek called the single-celled animals he had discovered *animalcules*. Today, they are called *protozoans*, which means *first animal*.

Observing Effects of Light on *Euglena*

DEMONSTRATION 1

Light is necessary for *Euglena* to live. In this demonstration you will observe how *Euglena* react to changes in the light around them.

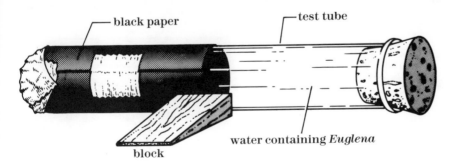

black paper — test tube — water containing *Euglena* — block

Set-up for Demonstration 1

1. A test tube is filled with pond water containing *Euglena* and secured in a horizontal position.
2. Half of the test tube is covered with black paper.
3. The uncovered portion of the test tube is exposed to light for several hours.
4. When the paper is removed, the portion of the test tube that was not covered is much greener than the covered portion.

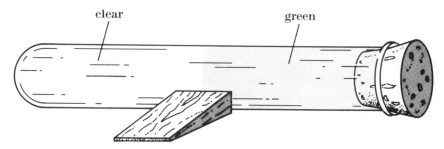

clear   green

Demonstration Results

Discussion

1. What is the purpose for covering a portion of the test tube with black paper?
2. What is the reason for placing the test tube horizontally and not vertically?
3. Explain what you observed.
4. Suggest reasons why the *Euglena* move to the illuminated part of the test tube.

DEMONSTRATION 2

Observing *Elodea* under Different Conditions

Like *Euglena*, *Elodea* needs light to live. You will see how *Elodea* reacts to different light conditions.

1. *Elodea* plants are set up as shown in figure 1 and figure 2. They are left for 24 h.

Figure 1   Figure 2

2. After 24 h the plants appeared as shown in figure 3 and figure 4.

Figure 3

Figure 4

Discussion

1. What was the difference in environment for the two plants?
2. Compare figure 3 and figure 4. Explain the difference between the leaf that was in the sunlight and the leaf that was in the cupboard.

Metabolism and Reproduction in Living Things

In order for living things to move and react, they need energy. One of the main reasons living things feed is to obtain the energy from what they eat. The major source of energy on the earth is sunlight. **Green plants**, those which generally contain chloroplastids, can change light energy from sunlight into the kind of energy found in food. The process by which green plants make this change is called **photosynthesis**. During photosynthesis, green plants produce not only food, but also a gas which is very important to most other living things. This gas is **oxygen**.

In Demonstration 2, bubbles appeared on the *Elodea* in the sunlight. These bubbles contain oxygen gas. Why do you think the plant kept in the dark did *not* produce oxygen?

Photosynthesis is an example of a characteristic of life called **metabolism**. Metabolism is the process by which living things use energy. This energy enables living things to do things like move and react. In other words, metabolism makes both movement and irritability possible.

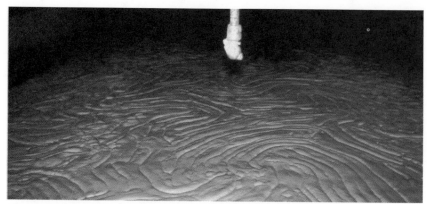

The fermentation stage in beer-making. The foam on the top is caused by carbon dioxide, a product of yeast metabolism.

Metabolism also makes it possible for living things to create other living things of their kind. This fourth characteristic of all living things is called **reproduction**. Cells like those in the *Elodea* plant reproduce by splitting into two new cells. A living thing must reproduce itself to ensure the survival of its kind.

You have used the microscope to help you see living things that are too small to see without magnification. In doing so, you have been able to see some examples of the four characteristics of life. These characteristics are metabolism, movement, irritability, and reproduction.

All living things share these four characteristics. Metabolism allows living things to use energy. Therefore, movement, irritability, and reproduction all depend on metabolism. Movement allows living things to feed, avoid danger, and find mates. Irritability allows living things to react to changes around them. Reproduction allows living things to create other living things of their kind.

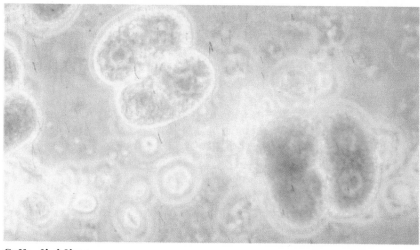

Cells dividing

Cancer Cells

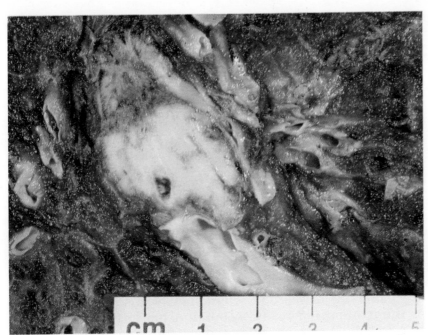

Close-up of a cancerous growth in lung tissue. The white area is the cancerous tumor.

In your body right now, cells are reproducing. Each cell divides to provide new cells for growth, to heal damaged tissue, and to replace cells that have worn out. Millions of normal cell divisions happen in your body every second. Occasionally, however, something goes wrong with this process. The result may be cancer.

Cancer begins when a cell reproduces itself too quickly. The resulting cells reproduce so quickly that the process is soon out of control. The growing mass of cancer cells, or the tumor, invades other parts of the body. But what causes that first cell to go wrong? Researchers are still looking for answers to this question.

The answers seem to lie within the nucleus of the cell. It is here that the cell's *blueprints* for reproduction are stored. In other words, something in the nucleus "tells" the cell when and how to reproduce itself. Sometimes this blueprint is changed. Scientists think this change may be caused by cancer-producers called *carcinogens*. You probably know about some carcinogens, such as cigarette smoke and industrial chemicals. Forms of energy from the sun, from nuclear accidents, or even from X rays might also be carcinogenic.

Forms of energy similar to these, however, can actually be used to treat cancer. Some powerful rays of energy are capable of destroying cancer cells and can save the lives of cancer patients. Doctors also use chemical treatments to kill cancer cells. As scientists gain more knowledge about cancer cells, cancer treatments will become more effective.

1. Make a list of five substances that are thought to cause cancer.
2. How can industrial chemicals that are thought to cause cancer be disposed of safely?
3. What steps would you take to reduce the risk of people being exposed to carcinogens?
4. Suggest three questions about smoking and cancer. Use these questions as the basis of a class debate.

2.3

Animal Cells and Plant Cells

Most living things you see are either animals or plants. Most plants stay anchored in one place, while most animals move around quite freely. Most plants are green, while most animals are not.

By using the microscope, scientists have discovered that living things are made up of tiny building blocks called cells. You are now going to use the microscope to observe some of the differences between the cells of an animal and the cells of a plant.

The Spanish moss hanging from the tree appears to be dead but is actually a living, flowering plant.

Observing Animal Cells

Your body is made of animal cells. In this activity, you will use a microscope to look at the cells found inside your mouth.

Materials

microscope
slide and coverslip
lens paper
toothpick
eyedropper
methylene blue solution (You can use an iodine solution if
    methylene blue is not available.)

Procedure

1. Using an eyedropper, place two drops of water in the centre of a clean slide.
2. Using a toothpick, *gently* scrape the inside of your mouth. *This will not hurt.*
3. At the end of the toothpick, you will see a tiny bit of material. Place this material in the drops of water on the slide. To do so, move the end of the toothpick through the water.
4. Place a coverslip over the specimen.
5. Place the slide on the stage of your microscope, over the hole in the stage.
6. Using first the low-power objective lens, and then the medium-power lens, observe the slide.
7. You are looking for cells that are colorless. Move the slide slowly back and forth until you see some of them.
8. Using one drop of methylene blue, instead of two drops of water, repeat steps 1 through 6.
9. Draw one cell in your notebook.

Discussion

1. Describe the shape of the cell.
2. Are all the cells you observed the same shape?
3. Compare your observations of the cells in the water with the cells in the methylene blue solution.

Can scientists make living cells from non-living material? Not yet, but they are trying to understand how the very first living cells came about. In order to do this, they first imagine what the earth was like many millions of years ago, before there were any plants and animals. They then try to recreate some of the events of that time in their laboratories. These same events might have led to the first living cells.

The Structures of an Animal Cell

Each animal cell contains many structures. In Activity 6, you were able to observe some of these structures with your microscope.

The watery substance that makes up most of the cell is called **cytoplasm**. The thin border surrounding the cytoplasm is the **cell membrane**. Just inside the membrane, you might see some small bubble-like structures which appear to be empty. These structures are called **vacuoles**.

The cell contains other kinds of structures as well. Many of them are invisible, even under the microscope. Stains such as methylene blue, used in Activity 6, are special chemicals that color the parts of the cell that are normally invisible. One of these structures is the **nucleus**. This structure is usually round and is found in the middle of the cell.

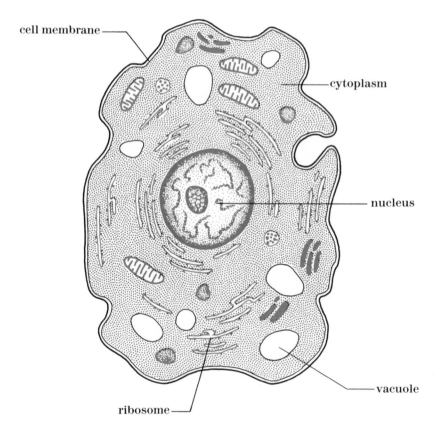

Structure of an animal cell

Observing Plant Cells

In this activity, you will observe cells found in an onion.

Materials

microscope
slide and coverslip
lens paper
eyedropper
tweezers
onion
methylene blue solution (or iodine solution)

Procedure

1. Using an eyedropper, place two drops of water in the middle of a glass slide.
2. Pick up one of the pieces of onion from your teacher. Your teacher will have cut the onion into quarters for you. Separate one of the fleshy leaves from the rest.

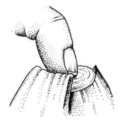

3. Hold the fleshy leaf as in the drawing. Remove a small portion from the surface of the fleshy leaf with tweezers.

4. Using tweezers, place the small portion of onion material into the water on the slide.
5. Place a coverslip over the specimen.
6. Using first the low-power objective lens, and then the medium-power lens, observe the specimen.
7. Draw one cell in your notebook.
8. Using a drop of iodine solution instead of water, repeat steps 1 through 6.

Discussion

1. Describe the shape of the plant cell.
2. What is the large, empty-looking oval in the middle of the plant cell?
3. What are the round, green structures called?
4. Compare your observations of the cells in the water with the cells in the methylene blue solution.

The Structures of a Plant Cell

Plant cells contain many structures. The thick outer boundary of the plant cell is called the **cell wall**. Only plant cells have cell walls. Animal cells do not. Like animal cells, certain parts of plant cells are colorless and are hard to see. When stains are added, the nucleus, located near the side of the cell, can be seen. Just inside the cell wall, a cell membrane is present. Vacuoles are also present in plant cells. Like animal cells, the watery substance making up most of the cell is cytoplasm.

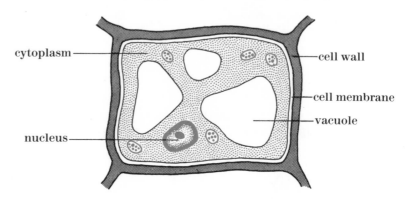

Structure of a Plant Cell

EXTENSION ACTIVITY

Building Cell Models

When you observe a cell using a microscope, it is difficult to see that the cell has depth as well as length and width. In other words, cells are not totally flat. In order to help you understand that cells have depth, you will now build a model of a plant cell and an animal cell.

1. Work with a partner. Decide who will build a model of an animal cell and who will build a model of a plant cell.
2. Choose any material you wish in order to make a three-dimensional model of a plant or animal cell. If you wish, use something like a shoebox or jelly. In your model, make sure that you show the various parts of the cell.

Questions

1. Label the drawings of the animal and the plant cell that you made in Activities 6 and 7. List the differences and the similarities between the two types of cells.
2. Only plants can carry out photosynthesis. What is present in plant cells, but not in animal cells, that makes photosynthesis possible?

Then

By viewing pond water first without magnification, then with a magnifying lens, and finally with a microscope, you have retraced centuries of scientific history. Before the invention of the microscope, scientists were only able to observe living things without using magnification. Medicine and other life sciences were severely limited by the inability to observe extremely fine detail.

The idea that all plants and animals are made up of cells is less than 175 years old. Yet the microscope is about 400 years old. In other words, the microscope was in use for over two centuries before cells were recognized as the basic unit of life. Why did this realization take so long?

A new discovery does not always have a clear, immediate purpose. Two sixteenth-century Dutch spectacles makers used two separate lenses to make the first microscope. Yet they had no real purpose for their invention. They made it because it was an interesting idea that nobody else had thought of trying. This kind of curiosity often leads to long-term scientific developments that the inventor never imagined.

A few decades later, the British scientist Robert Hooke reported the presence of cells for the first time. Around the same time, the self-taught Dutch scientist Anton van Leeuwenhoek discovered blood cells and single-celled plants and animals. The importance of these discoveries was not apparent at that time. The microscope and the cell were little more than topics for conversation at dinner.

Things did not change much during the following century and a half. In 1824, the French scientist Rene Dutrochet came to the conclusion that all plants and animals are made of cells. Over the twenty years that followed, a general *cell theory* was developed. The theory states, among other things, that the cell is the smallest unit of life that can reproduce itself.

Then and Now

Microscopes and Cells

**Small part of a spider's
rear foot**

**Interwoven wing
feathers of a bird**

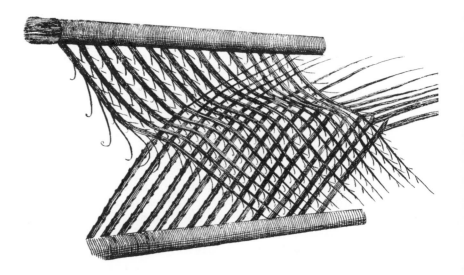

**Van Leeuwenhoek's drawings of what he saw through his
microscope**

Now

Microscopes like the kind you have seen in this chapter are
called *optical microscopes*. They use light to form an image of
an object. The most powerful optical microscopes can magnify
objects up to 500 times. Many specialized optical microscopes
have been developed for specific uses. Microscopes can also be
combined with other instruments.

The most powerful modern microscopes are called *electron
microscopes*. They use a beam of *electrons* instead of light to
form an image of an object. Because human eyes cannot see
electrons, the image is converted to a picture on a television
screen. Electron microscopes can magnify objects from
10 000–500 000 times.

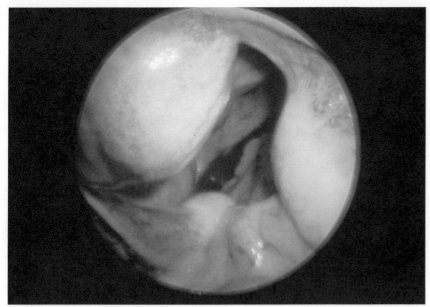

A specialized optical instrument for viewing the internal structure of the human body is called a laparascope. This is a laparascopic image of two ovaries (the round shapes).

A special kind of electron microscope, called an *analytical electron microscope*, can form an image of a specimen and can identify some of the substances contained in the specimen.

One of the most advanced kinds of analytical microscopes, called the *Ottensmeyer microscope*, was developed by Dr. Peter Ottensmeyer at the Ontario Cancer Institute to study cancer cells. This microscope can analyse substances 100 times smaller than any other electron microscope. It can identify atoms in a sample.

The Ottensmeyer microscope is being used around the world for various purposes such as analysis of computer chips and special metals as well as for medical research.

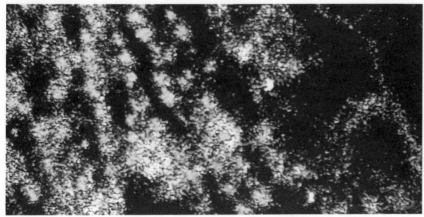

Seen through an electron microscope, the tiny, gold-colored structures are ribosomes.

Aerial view of a coastline showing macroscopic features. Macroscopic features are those that can be seen with the unaided eye.

Summary

Objects that cannot be seen by the unaided eye are called microscopic. Microscopic objects can be viewed with a magnifying glass or microscope. By observing pond water through the microscope, you can identify some characteristics of living things such as movement and irritability.

The main source of energy for living things is the sun. Green plants change light energy from the sun into the kind of energy found in food through a process called photosynthesis. Photosynthesis is an example of metabolism, a process in which living things use energy. Metabolism makes possible not only movement and irritability, but also reproduction.

Living things are made up of cells. A microscope reveals that both plant and animal cells have a cell membrane, vacuoles, a nucleus, and cytoplasm. However, only plant cells have a cell wall.

Chapter Questions

Remember

1. Label the parts of the microscope.
2. Which of the statements below are true? Which are false? Rewrite the false statements to make them true.
   a) In focussing a microscope, you use the coarse adjustment before the fine adjustment.

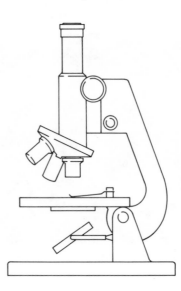

b)   The objective lens is the lens of the microscope through which you look.

c)   The shorter the objective lens is, the greater the enlargement of what you are viewing.

d)   Anything that moves is alive.

e)   Plants, but not animals, are capable of photosynthesis.

f)   Both animal and plant cells have cell membranes.

g)   Both animal and plant cells have cell walls.

3. Why must you use lens paper to clean the lens of a microscope?

4. Why do you need a coverslip when you are using the high-power objective lens?

5. Why are stains used to color specimens to be observed with the microscope?

Think

1. Why is the microscope important to biologists?
2. What is photosynthesis and why is it important?
3. How do *Euglena* benefit from their attraction to light?
4. List and describe the four characteristics of life.
5. State one major difference between plant and animal cells.

Dream

1. What information would you need to determine whether an imprint in a rock was once a living organism?
2. Suppose you saw a purple, slimy object move into a pond. How would you determine if it were alive?
3. In the introduction to this chapter, intelligent Martians observed the earth's inhabitants through a powerful telescope. How would you compare your observations in this chapter with the observations of the Martians?

Fossils are impressions or hard structures left in sediments that are compressed into rock. A fossilized leaf is shown here.

Decide

1. Observe and describe a pet. In your description, distinguish between your observations and your inferences.

a)   Beside each observation, state the characteristics of life that are being observed.

b)   Which of your inferences are based on your knowledge of characteristics of living things?

Making

Nutrition

What kinds of cells did you have for breakfast this morning? This might seem like a strange question, because you do not often think of food in this way. But the plants and animals that you use for food are all made up of many different kinds of cells. The types of cells that you eat have a direct effect on how well-nourished you are. What sorts of cells are most important for nutrition?

You are made up of animal cells. Therefore, animal cells would seem to be the most important for nutrition. A serving of fish, for example, is made up of muscle cells. These are similar in many ways to your own muscle cells. But when you eat a fish fillet, the muscle cells of the fish do not travel directly to your muscles. Instead, your digestive system breaks down the cells, releasing chemical nutrients. These nutrients then travel through the bloodstream to where they are needed.

Because they are very different from your cells, plant cells are nutritious in a different way. Proteins, the chemical building blocks of cells, are found in both plant and animal cells. Plant proteins are less useful to your body than animal proteins. But other vital nutrients, such as some vitamins and minerals, are abundant in plant cells.

The cells of many animals, including cows, are used as a source of nutrition for people.

The cell walls of plants are made up of cellulose, which is often called fibre. Fibre in the diet is extremely important to the proper functioning of the digestive tract. Scientists think it can even help prevent cancer in the digestive system. So be sure to eat your vegetables.

Vegetables are an important part of a healthy diet.

3

Classification

Imagine going to your favorite record store to find the latest recording by the group Mister Twister. When you get there, you are surprised to find that the store has new owners. The storefront now reads *Ace Unclassified* Records and Tapes. You decide to go inside and see just what is meant by the word *unclassified*.

Inside, you do not see the usual displays and racks of recordings. In the middle of the floor, you see instead a huge pile of records, cassettes, and compact discs. The pile looks as if it had been left there by a dump truck. When you ask if the new Mister Twister cassette has come in yet, the cashier points toward the pile and replies, "It's in there somewhere." But to find Mister Twister among the thousands of jumbled recordings in front of you would be nearly impossible. Now you understand what the word *unclassified* means, and why it is important to classify things.

Classification organizes things by grouping them into **sets**. Record stores often have more than 5000 recordings in stock, yet you can find the one you want in minutes. To find the Mister Twister cassette, you would simply go to the section of the store labelled "Rock," and look in the cassette racks under *M*. In this way, you would be using the store's system of classification. This is just one of the ways in which things can be classified.

In this chapter, you will learn about the process of classification in everyday life and in science. It is a process that makes it easier for you to gather, organize, and understand information. In this chapter, you will concentrate on ways to classify non-living things. In chapter 4, you will look at ways to classify living things.

3.1

Classification in Everyday Life

The recordings in these photographs can be classified in several ways. Imagine that you are the owner of a record store, and try to find a useful way to classify these records.

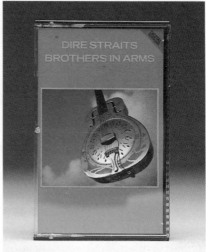

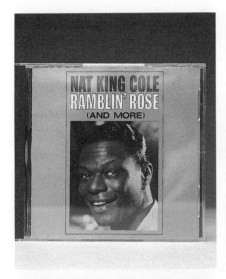

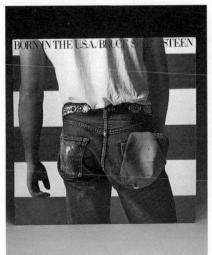

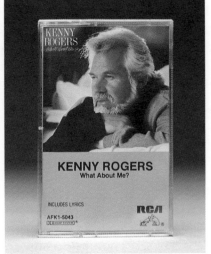

Making Your Own Classification System

In this activity, you will classify musical recordings brought from home. The method that you use to classify them will be your own.

Materials

recordings brought from home by each student and labelled with the owner's name

Procedure

1. Work in groups of three or four.
2. List the features of the recordings that you will use to classify them.
3. Now design your classification system. Put it on a large sheet of paper or Bristol board and sign it. Make a copy in your notes.
4. Post these classification systems around the room.
5. Look at the systems designed by all of the other groups. Compare them with your own group's design.
6. List any features that were different from your own.
7. Examine the recordings to see if any of them do not fit in your system. List these recordings in your notes.
8. Meet as a class to decide which features were most useful in the classification of your recordings. Create a new classification system based on the new features chosen.

Discussion

1. Which features were used by every group?
2. Which features were used less often?
3. Did your classification system organize all of the recordings? If not, how could it be improved in order to do so?
4. If a classification system organizes all of the recordings, is this system **a)** the only one possible? **b)** the best one possible?

Extension

1. Visit a tapes-and-records store near you and ask about the classification system used there. Ask for reasons why this system is used. Is it like yours?
2. Research Thomas Edison's first recording. Would it fit your classification system? If not, change your system.

Varieties of Classification

From Activity 1 you can see that there is more than one way to classify things. Classification systems of many kinds are used widely in our daily lives. Here are several examples.

Foods can be classified into different types.

Medicines can be classified by their uses.

Perfume ingredients can be classified by aroma.

You have probably used all of these classification systems. Imagine how difficult it would be to find a telephone number, look up an advertisement, or locate the book you want if none of these items were classified in some way.

You classify most things in your life. This is especially true of your interests.

When you want to classify objects like recordings, you first observe their similarities and differences. Recordings have properties that you can observe, such as size and shape. In Activity 1, you probably classified the record albums together and grouped cassettes separately. Size and shape are two simple observations that can help you classify objects.

Rock collections can be classified by the site where the rocks were found and by color, mineral content, and age.

But you probably further classified your recordings on the basis of other similarities and differences. You might have considered whether the recording artists were male or female, solo artists, or members of groups. You might have organized your recordings on the basis of the kind of music. You might have grouped the recordings chronologically, according to the years in which they were made; or alphabetically, by the first letter of the artist's name.

You might even have considered the different kinds of technology used to make records, cassettes, and compact discs.

Some recordings are pressed into vinyl discs.

Through the observation of similarities and differences in objects, groups of objects can be broken down into smaller and smaller sets. This classification is done in record stores. There might be one section of the store displaying records, another displaying cassettes, and still another displaying compact discs. Within the cassette section, there could be a smaller set of recordings that are classified as *Rock.* This set of rock cassettes could be classified in alphabetical order. One set within the rock cassettes would be the *M* set. One set within the *M* set could be the set that is made up of just the single Mister Twister cassette you were looking for.

Questions

1. Examine the white pages of a telephone book.
   a) Describe the first method used to organize all of the telephone numbers on this page.
   b) Describe the next method used.

    c)   Whose number comes first in a phone book?
- Glen Frost or Glen Forest
- Harold Crane or Helen Crane
- T.C. Chen or T. Chen

    d)   Which general observation is being used to organize a telephone book?

2. How are the yellow pages of a telephone book classified differently from the white pages?

3. One section of the paper is set aside for classified ads.

    a)   How are these advertisements first classified?

    b)   How are each of these sets then organized?

    c)   In particular, how are the used-car ads organized? Describe the system used.

    d)   Are all ads in the paper classified? Why or why not?

3.2

A Useful Classification System

The four kinds of cassette players shown here are arranged in no particular order.

4 Cassette Players

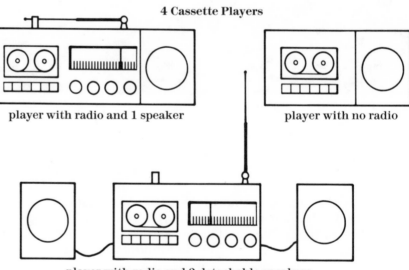

player with radio and 1 speaker   player with no radio

player with radio and 2 detachable speakers

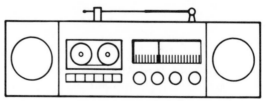

player with radio and 2 built-in speakers

The same cassette players are classified here according to certain features.

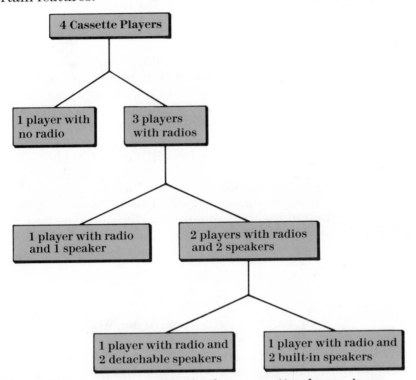

The system used to classify the four cassette players is an example of **dichotomous classification**. Dichotomous means divided into two. Dichotomous classification works by dividing information or objects into two sets. The sets that have more than one item in them are then re-divided until each set has only one member. This division is done by using an observation to make an *either/or* judgment.

The four cassette players were first divided into two sets. One set had cassette players with built-in radios. The other set did not. The set with built-in radios was then re-divided into two sets, according to whether the cassette players had two speakers or one speaker. Finally, the set containing cassette players with built-in radios and two speakers was broken down into two sets of one: one cassette player had detachable speakers; the other had built-in speakers.

A **dichotomous key** such as the one just used shows you how classified groups are related to each other. The key can take the form of a series of questions. For example, consider a classification system for shoes. You could ask whether the shoes were intended for male or female use. This question would divide the shoes into two sets. Then each set could be divided by asking whether the shoes were formal or informal. This second division could be divided into four smaller sets. The process can be continued until every shoe is classified separately.

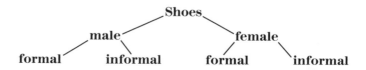

In dichotomous classification, it is important to ask a question that both *separates the objects into two groups* and *includes all objects within the set*. Try to classify a set of a dozen pairs of shoes by color. For example, five pairs of shoes are brown, four are white, two are blue, and one is red. The three figures below show three possible classifications on the basis of color. Only one of these classifications is dichotomous.

This figure shows a dichotomous key. This key does the two things that any dichotomous key must do. It divides the set into two and includes every member of the set. If you had divided the set in a similar way, for example, brown shoes and non-brown shoes, that key would also make a dichotomous classification.

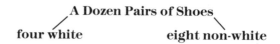

This figure also represents a key that includes every member of the set. This, however, is not a dichotomous key. It divides the set into four sets, not into two sets.

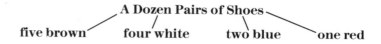

This figure represents a key that would not be suitable for classification. It does make a division into two, but these divisions would not include all the members of the set. Three of the twelve pairs would not be included.

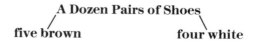

Making a Dichotomous Key

In this activity, you will design a dichotomous key to classify common objects.

Materials

The materials to be used will already be available at school. You may choose any one of the following or make a choice of your own.

shoes worn to class
clothes worn to class
jewellery worn to class
writing instruments

Procedure

1. Choose the materials you will classify and make a list of all of the items.
2. Decide on the observation you will use to begin your dichotomous key.
3. Classify your materials based on this observation.
4. Continue choosing observations and classifying until every item is separated.
5. Check your key by choosing one object. Starting from the top of your key, classify your object. Make certain that it is classified correctly throughout the key.
6. Draw a diagram for your classification key. Show only the choices to be made, not the objects chosen. Label it *Dichotomous Key for (your materials)*.
7. Exchange your key with other students. Use their key to classify their materials.
8. Check each other's results. If any mistakes were made, discuss them to see if the fault is with the key. If so, correct the key.

Discussion

1. Is your key complete? Are there any examples of similar materials which were not at school and would not fit into your key?
2. Now that you have used someone else's dichotomous key, are there any disadvantages that you can see with this type of classification key? Discuss them.
3. Can you see some patterns in the materials that you used? For example, are certain types of this material more common at school than somewhere else?

Extension

1. Design a dichotomous system to classify all of the appliances in your home. Include large appliances such as refrigerators and stoves, and small ones like blenders and curling irons.

Questions

1. Define a dichotomous key.
2. Construct a dichotomous key to classify a personal collection, for example, shells or hockey cards.

What types of classification systems can be used in shopping malls?

3. Give three examples of systems used in everyday life that are **a)** dichotomous **b)** non-dichotomous.

Although it would be a huge task, you could create a dichotomous system for classification of the entire universe. Imagine that you were programming a computer to classify the huge number of things involved. This figure will help to get you started.

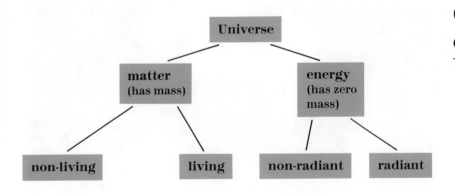

3.3

Dichotomous Classification of the Universe

To complete the task would take a great deal of time and knowledge. Other chapters in this book can give you some of the necessary information.

3.4

Dichotomous Classification of Non-living Matter

There are a great many forms of non-living matter to classify. Some examples are shown below.

Group 1	Group 2
water	cardboard
air	steel
clouds	denim
stars	gold
vinegar	ice
soft drink	aluminum
Freon	nylon
drain cleaner	rubber

Perhaps you can see the property that makes the two groups different. The materials in group 1 are fluids. Those in group 2 are solids. All non-living matter can be divided into fluids and solids.

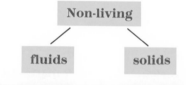

Can you classify this common dessert?

Dry ice is solid carbon dioxide. When a piece of dry ice is added to a beaker of water, the solid changes into carbon dioxide gas. This gas forms bubbles in the water. When the gas spills out of the beaker, it has no specific shape.

Fluids are materials which flow. They do not have a specific shape. Instead, they take the shape of the container that holds them. Water is a fluid. So is air.

Solids have a specific shape. They do not flow. If you push your finger against a rock, the whole rock moves. If you push water, or any other fluid, it flows around your finger.

Of course, water is only a fluid at room temperature. When it is cold enough, water changes to a solid. Similarly, rock will flow when it is heated above its melting point. Our classification system only accounts for the usual states of these materials.

Liquid rock (lava) flowing out of the earth during an eruption on a Hawaiian island

Fluids can be divided further into liquids and gases.

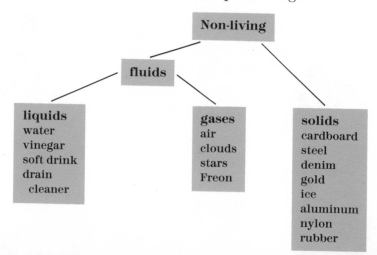

A fluid in both its liquid and gaseous forms occupies the volume of its container. Bromoform and bleach were combined to produce this reaction.

Gases spread out to fill the entire container. Liquids settle in the bottom of a container.

Solids can be divided into two types. They are either metals or non-metals.

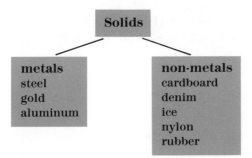

Metals can carry electric currents. They are usually shiny and can be bent into new shapes. Non-metals are dull and often brittle.

This dichotomous classification of non-living matter is summarized in this figure. Remember this is only one way to design a classification scheme. Other systems may prove more useful as you learn more about the properties of matter.

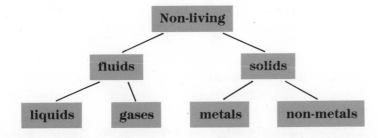

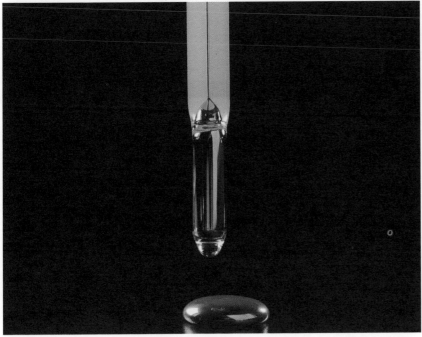

Not all metals can be easily classified. For instance, unlike other metals, mercury is liquid at room temperature.

ACTIVITY 3

Presenting a Dichotomous Key

In this activity, you will use a visual display to represent a dichotomous key.

Materials

pictures of non-living objects
at least four duplicates of each picture
Bristol board
glue
scissors

Procedure

1. Decide whether your project will be an individual display, a group display, or a display involving the entire class.
2. Plan a dichotomous key for your collection of non-living things.
3. Make sure that you have at least one picture for each category of the dichotomous key.
4. Starting with the category *All Things*, put one picture of each object under this label.
5. Divide one duplicate set of pictures into two smaller sets. Label each smaller set and glue the appropriate duplicate pictures in place. Continue to divide each set in two until there is only one picture in each set.
6. Use lines to connect the sets.
7. Set up your display where other students in the school can see it.

Extension

1. Make the display from Activity 3 into a game. To do so, remove some pictures of objects, along with their labels. Shuffle the pictures you have removed from the display. Challenge a classmate to place them in the correct set and to provide a label.
2. Make the original display without pictures. Put descriptions of the contents of each set under each label. Challenge your classmates to place the pictures in the correct set.

Questions

1. How are fluids different from solids?
2. How are liquids different from gases?
3. Classify the materials in the following list on the basis of the second figure on page 79. You may have to research the properties of some of these if you are not familiar with them. Assume that they are at room temperature.

    a) copper   **e)** paper
    b) carbon dioxide   **f)** Silly Putty
    c) salt   **g)** ashes
    d) Teflon   **h)** mercury

Summary

Classification is one way of organizing information or materials. Everyone classifies things in order to make them easier to find, to use, and to understand.

Many classification systems can be designed for the same information. The choice depends on the purpose of the system.

Dichotomous classification uses a dichotomous key to divide things into sets. The key is a series of *either/or* choices. Each choice divides things in a set into two smaller sets. This kind of system is best for finding similarities and differences between things.

Non-living matter can be classified dichotomously. All non-living matter is either a fluid or a solid. In turn, all fluids are either liquids or gases, while all solids are either metals or non-metals.

Computers "think" by turning electronic switches on or off. Since there are only these two settings, all information is recorded in a dichotomous way.

Chapter Questions

Remember

1. Give four examples of classification systems used in everyday life.
2. What is dichotomous classification? State an example of a decision in a dichotomous system.
3. Match each item in column A with an item from column B to make an *either/or* dichotomous classification.

A	B
matter	liquid
synthetic	energy
solid	natural
gas	fluid

Think

1. Why is classification useful in the following?
   a) everyday life   **b)** science
2. Classify one or more of the following. Use either a dichotomous or a non-dichotomous system.

a) the clothes in your closet
b) the appliances in your house
c) the letters in the alphabet
d) the keys in your house

3. Describe a possible next step in the divisions of metals on page 79.

4. Reorganize the classification system for non-living things discussed in this chapter into a non-dichotomous but useful form.

5. On page 64 you were asked to classify eight samples of recorded music. One possible dichotomous classification system for the recordings is shown here. Suggest some others.

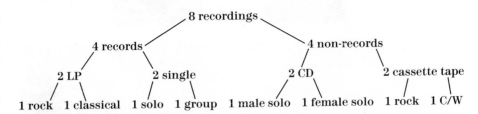

6. Find out how resource materials, such as books, are classified.

Dream

1. Find a book about unidentified flying objects in the library. Design a classification system for UFOs.

Decide

1. Why is a dichotomous system not used to classify records in a record store? In fact, what is the major drawback of the dichotomous method?

Classification in Astronomy

Science-fiction movies depict worlds of many types, such as desert planets and jungle moons. If you were an astronomer, how would you classify planets and moons?

Some planets may not have solid surfaces like the earth. Jupiter is called a gas giant because it is a huge ball of gas that appears to have no real surface. The smaller, earth-like bodies in the solar system are made of solid materials.

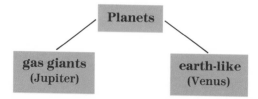

Mars is an earth-like planet. This is an artist's concept of a future space colony on Mars.

The surface material of earth-like planets can be mainly rocky or mainly icy. Spacecraft have shown Venus to be an unbelievably hot, rocky desert. Other space probes have photographed frozen worlds made mostly of ice, for example, Jupiter's moon, Europa.

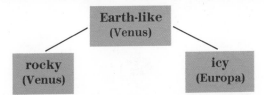

Earth-like
(Venus)

rocky
(Venus)

icy
(Europa)

These are examples of dichotomous systems that you could use to classify bodies of the solar system. You could also classify bodies according to the kinds of objects around which they orbit. Jupiter is classified as a planet because it orbits the sun. Europa is classified as a moon because it revolves around a planet. Can you think of any other ways of classifying objects in the solar system?

No one has ever seen the planet Jupiter's surface. This photograph shows the dense atmosphere that hides everything beneath.

This drawing shows the highest known point on the surface of the planet Venus. This mountain is 10.8 km high, much higher than Mount Everest.

Connections

4

Classification of Living Things

If you have ever been to a zoo, you might have noticed that some of the most popular animals are the apes. People crowd around to watch them play, climb trees or fences, or peel and eat fruit. Perhaps people find apes so interesting because they seem so much like humans. They have fun, get upset, and have friendships and family relationships much like humans do.

Scientists have found that apes and humans share many important characteristics. You can see, for example, how a chimpanzee skilfully uses its hands for eating and grooming. But scientists have been able to show that a chimpanzee cannot twiddle its thumbs like you can. The parts of a chimpanzee's hands are arranged differently than a human's hands. In other words, the structure of a chimpanzee's hands is different than a human's hands. Scientists use similarities in structure to classify living things.

Chimpanzees and humans are two similar forms of life. When you look at a sparrow in an apple tree, the similarities between the bird and the tree are not as obvious. The sparrow and the apple tree do not share as many characteristics as chimpanzees and humans do. When scientists classify living things, they group life forms, such as humans and chimpanzees, that have similar structures. Plants like apple trees are grouped separately from animals like sparrows.

In chapter 3, you discovered how important classification is. Organizing information helps you to understand the world. In the same way, classifying living things according to their similarities and differences in structure helps you to understand life. How could you classify sparrows and apple trees? How could you classify humans and chimpanzees? In this chapter, you will explore some of the ways in which living things have been classified.

Life is found in a variety of shapes and sizes.

a) Sea anemone

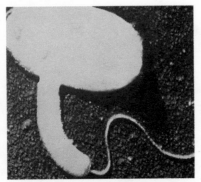

b) Single-celled animal

c) Sponge

d) Grapes

e) Rhinoceros

f) Long-horned beetle

Our prehistoric ancestors needed to understand their environment in order to survive. They knew that some animals, such as antelopes, could be hunted more safely than others. They also knew that they had to avoid dangerous animals, such as lions. In the same way, they knew that some plants were edible, while others were poisonous. For early humans, recognition of certain kinds of living things was often a matter of life and death.

If prehistoric hunters saw a kind of animal they had never seen before, maybe a cheetah, they would need to decide whether to hunt it or run away from it. By observing that the cheetah looked a little like a lion, the hunters might have decided to keep away from it. In this way, the hunters would be using similarities between the lion and the cheetah to get information about an unknown animal. The hunters would be classifying lions and cheetahs together as dangerous animals with claws and fangs.

Classification helped early humans to survive. But our ancestors were also simply curious about their environment. This curiosity led them to seek and classify information about

4.1

Early Classification of Living Things

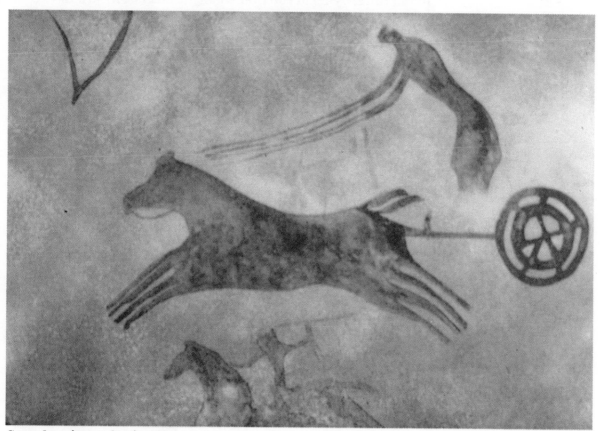

Cave drawings of animals

Aristotle

living things. One of the first widely used classification schemes was devised about twenty-three centuries ago by the Greek philosopher Aristotle. He classified plants and animals separately.

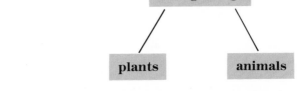

Aristotle classified plants according to the type of stem they had. Plants with soft stems he classified as herbs; those with more than one stem, as shrubs; and those with a single major stem, as trees.

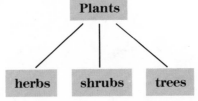

His classification system for animals was based on where they lived. He decided that all animals could be found on land, in the water, or in the air.

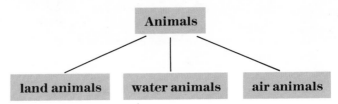

How useful would Aristotle's system be for classifying plants? How useful would it be for classifying animals? In the following two activities, you will try to answer these questions.

Classifying Plants

In this activity, you will classify plants found in the schoolyard or around your home. To do so, you will use Aristotle's classification system.

Materials

drawing pens or pencils
sketching paper

Procedure

1. Make a table like the one below.

Plant	Plant Name	Classification	Reason for Decision
1	dandelion	herb	soft stem

2. In the schoolyard, or at home, observe the shapes of six plants. Sketch the plants. Pay special attention to the different kinds of stems. Try to choose plants that are clearly different from each other.

3. Classify the six plants as herbs, shrubs, or trees.

A typical Canadian forest scene

Seed pods of a milkweed

Dandelion field

Discussion

1. What difficulties did you have in classifying these plants?
2. On the basis of Aristotle's system, could you distinguish between the following? Why or why not?
   a) a maple tree and an evergreen tree
   b) grass and mushrooms
3. How would you modify Aristotle's classification system in order to make the distinctions in question 2?

ACTIVITY 2

Classifying Mythical Creatures

Like modern tales of science fiction, many ancient stories refer to strange, imaginary creatures. Such stories, or myths, were an important part of the culture of Aristotle's time. In this activity, you will classify some of the creatures found in the myths of ancient Greece.

Materials

pictures of mythical creatures

Procedure

1. Substituting the names of the mythical creatures for the names of plants, make a table like that in Activity 1 on page 91.
2. Using your table, classify each of the creatures shown on page 92 according to whether they live on land, in the water, or in the air. Keep in mind all of the characteristics of each creature. Be sure to include reasons for your decisions.

Discussion

1. Compare your table with those of your classmates. Discuss the decisions you made in classifying the creatures.
   a) Which ones were based on structure?
   b) Which ones were based on other characteristics?
   c) What were these characteristics?
2. Do you think that Aristotle's classification system is useful? Why or why not?
3. Is Aristotle's classification system dichotomous? Explain your answer.

Questions

1. How would Aristotle classify these plants?
   a) cypress tree
   b) lichen
   c) rooted lily pad

Cypress tree

Lichen

Rooted lily pad

2. How would Aristotle classify these animals?

a) Frog

b) Penguin

c) Duck

d) Alligator

e) Newt

f) Hippopotamus

g) Seal

h) Flying squirrel

Aristotle's system of classifying living things was not perfect, but it was popular. For the purpose of the ancient Greeks, it seemed to work well. In fact, it was used by scientists for many centuries after Aristotle.

In Activity 2, you probably had difficulty deciding where some of the creatures lived. Pegasus had wings for flying and hoofs for running. The mermaid had fins instead of legs, but did not have gills. It needed air to breathe. The same is true for whales and dolphins. Problems like these make the classification of animals difficult within Aristotle's system. Classification of living things according to where they live is not the best method.

Scientists today classify living things according to their structural characteristics. Whales and dolphins, for example, are not classified as fish because of where they live. They are more closely related structurally to land animals, because they breathe air. They are structurally very different from fish. In the same way, penguins are classified as birds, not as fish. Their flippers are actually special kinds of wings. The fact that penguins also breathe air is another clue to suggest that they are not fish.

Classification is often easier when only two options are used. As you remember from chapter 3, this method involving *either/or* statements is called a dichotomous classification. Dichotomous keys, such as the ones you developed in chapter 3, can be useful for identification of living things.

4.2

Modern Classification of Living Things

Classifying Insects and Spiders

In this activity, you will make a dichotomous key for the classification of some insects and spiders.

ACTIVITY 3

Spider

Fly

Ant

Butterfly

Materials

pictures of insects and spiders

Procedure

1. Make a dichotomous key like the one below.

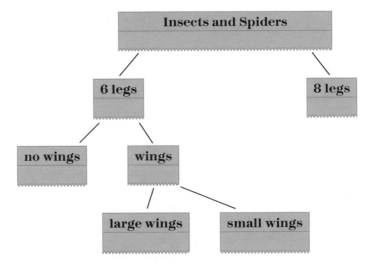

2. Observe the different characteristics of the insects and spiders shown in this activity.

3. Write the names of the animals in the appropriate box in your table.

Discussion

1. What characteristic of all spiders make them easy to distinguish from all insects?

2. Beetles are a common kind of insect. They usually have small wings that are hidden under protective covers when not in use. How could you revise your key to include insects with *small covered wings* and *large covered wings*?

Tiger beetle

Extension

1. Make up a dichotomous key to classify each of these groups of four animals.
   a) gerbil, guinea pig, squirrel, chipmunk
   b) duck, goose, chicken, turkey
2. Make an insect collection. Using a reference book, such as a field guide, classify the insects.

Classifying Leaves

ACTIVITY 4

In this activity, you will classify different kinds of evergreen leaves. As in the previous activity, you will use a dichotomous key.

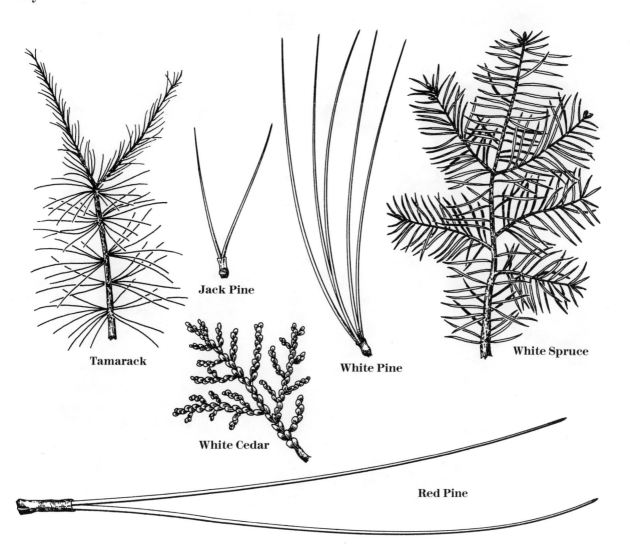

Jack Pine

Tamarack

White Cedar

White Pine

White Spruce

Red Pine

Materials

pictures of evergreen leaves

Procedure

1. Observe the different characteristics of the leaves shown on page 97.
2. Use this key to identify each of the leaves.

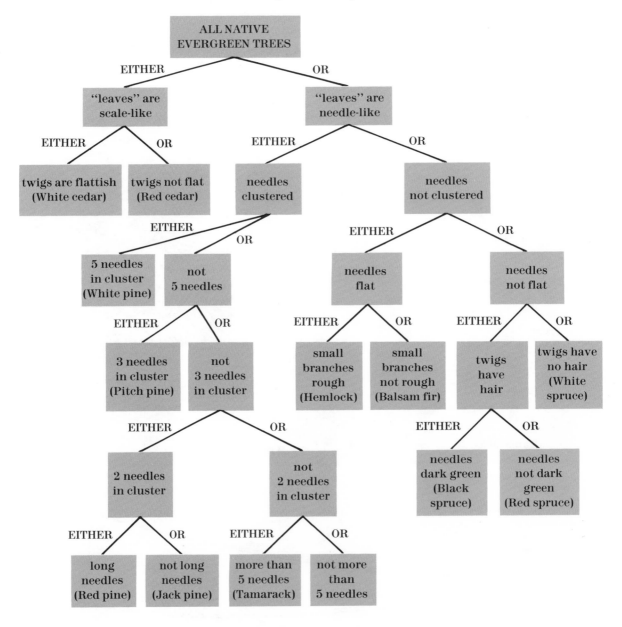

Key for Identifying Evergreen Leaves

Discussion

1. What characteristics of evergreen leaves were used in the key on page 98?

Extension

1. Wheat, barley, white beans, and soybeans are common field crops. Make up a dichotomous key for them.
2. Collect different kinds of leaves from trees around your home or school. Attempt to classify them.

Living things are divided into a few large groups. Within each large group, the members have certain structural similarities. One popular classification system has five large groups, each of which is called a kingdom. The five kingdoms include **Monerans**, **Protists**, **Fungi**, **Plants**, and **Animals**. Here are some of the major characteristics of the members of each kingdom.

Kingdom	Distinctive Characteristics
Monerans	microscopic; no cell nucleus
Protists	microscopic; cell nucleus
Fungi	plant-like; not green, no leaves
Plants	green; leaves, stems, and roots
Animals	mobile; have digestive and nervous systems

4.3

The Five Kingdoms of Living Things

Classifying Living Things into the Five Kingdoms

ACTIVITY 5

In this activity, you will classify five living things into the five kingdoms.

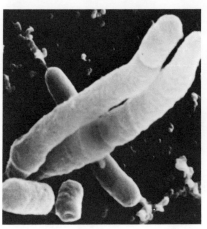

E.coli bacteria

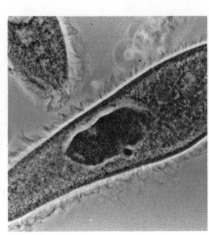

Paramecium

Fungi (mushrooms)

Crap apple tree

Sparrow

Materials

pictures of living things

Procedure

1. Make a key like the one below.

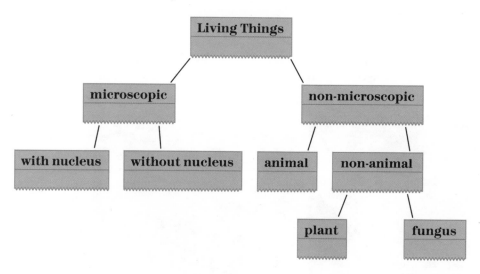

2. Observe the different characteristics of the five living things shown in this activity.

3. Write the names of the living things in the appropriate box in your key.

Discussion

1. Some scientists classify living things into fewer kingdoms than you just did. Try to classify the same living things into three kingdoms instead of five. What number of kingdoms do you think works better? Why?

You have now solved part of the problem set out at the beginning of the chapter. You have classified the apple tree within the plant kingdom and the sparrow within the animal kingdom. You have seen that living things belonging to different kingdoms have important structural differences.

The other part of the problem was to classify humans and chimpanzees. But they both belong to the animal kingdom. Clearly, the key you have worked with in Activity 5 does not go far enough. The animal kingdom must be broken into smaller groups.

Chimpanzees and humans belong to a group of animals called **Primates**. All apes, monkeys, and humans belong to this group. The primate group is just one of the hundreds of groups that make up the animal kingdom. How are chimpanzees and humans classified within this group?

4.4

Classification of Primates

Classifying Some Primates

In this activity, you will classify some primates, including humans and chimpanzees.

ACTIVITY 6

Bearded Guenon
(monkey)

Baboon (monkey)

Chimpanzee

Human

Baboon

Orangutan

Materials

pictures of primates

Procedure

1. Make a key like the one below.

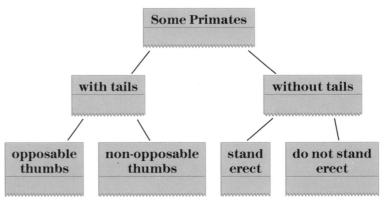

2. Observe the different characteristics of the four primates shown on page 101.

3. Write the names of the primates in the appropriate box in your key.

Discussion

1. Baboons, chimpanzees, and humans all have opposable thumbs. Why is this a useful characteristic?

2. The human is the only primate that can walk upright. How does this affect our ability to carry things from place to place? Why do you think this might be important?

Extension

1. Using a reference book, compare the classifications of humans and chimpanzees.

Summary

Classification is useful in many ways.

Aristotle devised one of the first widely used classification systems. He classified animals according to where they lived and plants according to their structure.

Modern classification systems are based on similarities and differences in structure.

One system for classifying living things divides all living things into five kingdoms. Within the animal kingdom, one group is known as primates. Humans are members of this group.

Chapter Questions

Remember

1. Give one example of a living thing within each of the five kingdoms.
2. What characteristic distinguishes humans from other primates?

Think

1. Compare Aristotle's classification system for living things with the modern five-kingdom system. Why do scientists no longer use Aristotle's system?

Dream

1. Suppose a visitor from another planet observed a collection of stuffed animals. The collection represented all the different kinds of cats and dogs. How would you explain to the visitor the differences between cats and dogs? Be sure your explanation accounts for all the varieties of each animal.

Decide

1. What additional knowledge or instruments would Aristotle have needed in order to arrive at the five-kingdom classification system used today?

Making

Fur, Feathers, and Scales

Have you ever seen a hairy snake? Can you image seeing a cat that has feathers instead of fur?

If you saw an animal that looked like a white pigeon, you might not know that it was a dove. But you would know that it was a bird of some kind, because you know that only birds have feathers. It is often useful to classify animals by their body covering.

Creatures from the film *Star Wars*

If you look closely at a bird's legs and feet, you can see how tough and scaly they appear. You might think that the covering on a bird's leg is like the body covering of a snake. Snakes and other reptiles have scales as their body covering. Birds are related to reptiles.

Pterodactyl dinosaur

Fish also have scales. But other waterdwellers have different body coverings. Lobsters have a hard shell-like exoskeleton, like insects. A shellfish, like a lobster, does not have bones like a fish does. It *wears* its skeleton on the outside.

Whales and dolphins do not have scales. Their body covering is something like your own. Even though they do not have fur, their skin is very similar to that of animals with fur. In fact, whales and dolphins are not fish. Whales and dolphins need air to breathe. Their distant ancestors were land animals.

As you can see, body coverings can help you to classify animals. Animals with feathers are birds. Reptiles and fish have scales. Like insects, lobsters and other shellfish have exoskeletons. You can tell that whales and dolphins are not fish, because they do not have scales.

In your school library, read about the duck-billed platypus. Do you think that this animal is more like a duck or a beaver? Explain your answer.

Crab, showing its exoskeleton

Killer whale and baby

Connections

5

Physical Change

When you make juice from frozen concentrate, you can control the amount of water you use. You can make your juice as weak or as strong as you like. When you buy juices in a ready-to-drink form, you have no way of knowing how much they have been watered down.

Tomato juice is one example of a ready-to-drink juice. The ingredient list on the label of the container does not tell you exactly how much water you are buying, or how many tomatoes. How could you test your tomato juice to see how much water is in it?

You might try passing the juice through a fine filter to catch the tomato pulp. You would find that the water that had gone through the filter would still be pink. You could filter the pink water again, but the water would never be pure. It would always have some tomato material in it, even if you could not see this material.

In this chapter, you will discover ways to separate pure substances out of mixtures like tomato juice. You will discover that you can often use these methods to find out what substances make up an unknown mixture. The processes you will use are the same ones often used to identify unknown substances.

5.1

Changes in Matter

Before pouring yourself a glass of tomato juice, you might shake the container to mix the juice more evenly. What happens if you do the same thing to a carbonated soft drink? Shaking can change different liquids in different ways.

Matter can be identified by the way it changes under certain conditions. Shaking is one example of a condition that can cause a substance to change. Heating is another. A metal cookie sheet, for example, would look the same after being in a hot oven for 1 h. A plastic platter, however, would not. Some plastics melt under such conditions and eventually burn.

In Activity 1, you will observe two kinds of change in matter.

Both uncut diamond (*left*) and mica (*right*) can be changed by splitting them along planes of weakness.

Heating Paraffin and Burning a Candle

Most candles are made from paraffin. In this activity, you will observe what happens when a candle is burned.

Materials

a candle
fireproof pad
400-mL beaker or other small glass container
pair of tongs or oven gloves

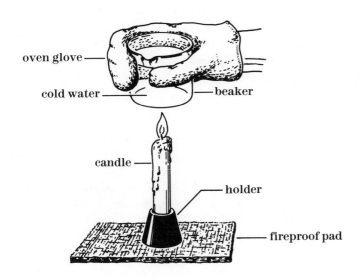

Procedure

1. Observe the candle. Write down your observations.
2. Light the candle. Observe and record any changes that occur as it burns.
3. Fill the beaker with cold water. Make sure that the outside of the beaker is dry.
4. Using the tongs or gloves, hold the beaker and lower it slowly toward the top of the flame.
5. Observe and record any changes on the surface of the beaker.
6. Empty the beaker and repeat steps 3, 4, and 5 several times.
7. Place the same beaker directly in the tip of the flame of the candle and remove it immediately.
8. Observe the bottom of the beaker.
9. Carefully tilt the candle so that some of the melted paraffin falls on a piece of paper. Observe the paraffin before and after it hits the paper. Record your observations.

Discussion

1. What happened to the candle as it burned?
2. Where did the matter from the candle go as it burned?
3. a) What substances appeared on the outside of the cool beaker when it was held above the candle flame? in the candle flame?
   b) Where did the substances come from and how did they get there?
4. Could you reverse the changes that occurred when the candle burned? In other words, could you collect all the substances given off by the candle and turn them back into a candle?
5. Could you remake the candle from the melted paraffin that you collected on the paper? Try it.

Extension

1. Do this test to identify the substance that appeared on the outside of the cool beaker when it was held above the flame. Sprinkle a small quantity of anhydrous copper sulphate on the substance. If it turns blue, water is present. Confirm that this test works by testing some water, alcohol, and glycerine in foil cups. Only the water should cause the anhydrous copper sulphate to turn blue.

Physical Changes and Chemical Changes

In Activity 1, you observed two different kinds of change in matter. When your candle burned, it produced new substances. The droplets that you saw on the cool beaker were water, and the black smudge on the beaker was carbon. Carbon dioxide gas, which is invisible, was also produced.

As the candle burned, it got smaller. If you kept burning the candle, the paraffin from which the candle was made would have eventually all disappeared. You can represent this particular change by using a **word equation**.

$$\text{paraffin} + \text{oxygen} \longrightarrow \text{carbon dioxide} + \text{water}$$

This kind of change, in which one substance disappears and is replaced with other substances, is called a **chemical change**. When a chemical change takes place, you actually end up with substances different from the ones you started with. Chemical changes are often useful for identifying substances. Hydrogen and helium gases are both clear, color-less, and lighter than air. But hydrogen gas burns, while helium does not, making it possible to tell them apart.

When the paraffin was melted, the change that occurred did not produce a different substance, even though the liquid paraffin had a different appearance. When allowed to cool, the paraffin did not regain the same shape as the candle you started with. Yet it did have the same color, texture, and feel. If you had wanted to, you could have reshaped the cooled paraffin into a candle, inserted a wick, and burned the original candle.

The heating of the paraffin caused it to change from a solid to a liquid. This change is an example of a **physical change**. A physical change alters the properties of a substance. In a physical change, no new substance is produced. The rest of this chapter will deal with physical changes. You will learn about chemical changes in chapter 6.

Questions

1. Classify the following as physical or chemical changes. In each case, give reasons for your answer.

   a) melting ice   **e)** making a snowball
   b) burning paper   **f)** dissolving sugar in water
   c) cooking a hamburger   **g)** a green apple ripening
   d) bending a metal rod   **h)** boiling a kettle of water

2. A friend tells you, "A chemical change can't be reversed, so that means that a baseball breaking a window is a chemical change." Explain to your friend why this is not true.

Does the blowing of glass represent a physical or chemical change?

3. Give some examples that show why it is sometimes difficult to tell the difference between physical and chemical changes.

4. Can you think of any changes to matter that do not appear to be either physical or chemical? Why do they not fit into this classification?

5.2

Three States of Matter

All matter can exist as a **solid**, a **liquid**, or a **gas**. These are called **states of matter**. The state in which matter occurs depends on the conditions around it. In Activity 1, you saw paraffin in two states. It was a solid when it was cool, and a liquid when it was hot. The third state of matter, gas, or **vapor**, is often invisible. Air is an example of an invisible gas. Solids and liquids have their own special properties. How are solids, liquids, and gases different? How are they similar?

Balloons filled with air can come in different shapes, and can be reshaped. You may have seen people make toy animals out of inflated balloons. The shape of an inflated balloon depends on the way the rubber of the balloon is shaped. Air itself has no shape. It takes the shape of its container, the rubber balloon. The same is true of all gases.

Liquids are also shaped by their containers. But liquids differ from gases in a very important way. Gases can be compressed, while liquids cannot. In other words, the volume of a gas can change, while that of a liquid cannot. These characteristics of gases and liquids are often used in technology. Some automobile shock absorbers use a column of compressed gas as a spring. But because liquids are not compressible, a shock absorber filled with a liquid would be too rigid to work. On the other hand, liquids work much better than gases for machine hydraulic systems, which transfer energy through pipes and hoses.

Hydraulic systems like this hydraulic hoist use liquids to transfer energy.

Solids, like liquids, cannot be compressed. In other words, solids also have fixed volumes. But while liquids and gases have variable shapes, solids have fixed shapes. Sand, for example, is made of rock. A rock has a fixed shape, but the shape of a handful of sand is variable. This does not mean that sand is not made of solid material. Even though the handful of sand acts like a liquid, each grain of sand has the properties of a solid.

These properties of the three states of matter are summarized in the following table.

Property	Solids	Liquids	Gases
shape	fixed	variable	variable
volume	fixed	fixed	variable

Questions

1. List ten substances that you normally encounter in one state, but which can occur in other states.
2. Can a chair be made out of gas? How might this be done?
3. Name three objects that are made from solids. Explain why they are made from solids. Consider whether the same device could be made from a liquid. Would it be possible? Why?
4. Lubricants such as motor oil usually come in a liquid form. Why? Could they come as solids or gases?

5. Solder used with a soldering iron is bought as a solid. How can it be made into a liquid?

6. How does the three-part classification of non-living matter you have seen in this chapter compare with the classification used on page 78?

5.3

Changes of State

Now that you have seen some of the properties of solids, liquids, and gases, you can explore changes in these states. A **change of state** is any physical change in the appearance, volume, and possibly the shape of a substance. No new substance is produced.

When you heated the paraffin in Activity 1, you saw that it changed from a solid state to a liquid state. This physical change is a change of state called **melting**.

Because changes of state do not destroy the original substance, they may be used to separate pure substances out of mixtures. In Activities 2 and 3, you will observe some other changes of state. Could you use any of them to separate water from tomato juice?

The melting of chocolate is a familiar change of state.

Heating Ice

In this activity, you will make observations of physical
changes of different states of matter and record what you see.
Observations can sometimes be shown in the form of graphs.
This activity will give you the opportunity to prepare a graph
of your observations. Your graph will help you to understand
what your observations mean.

Materials

crushed ice
thermometer
stirring rod
250-mL beaker
support stand
alcohol burner (or other source of heat)
graph paper
watch or clock showing seconds

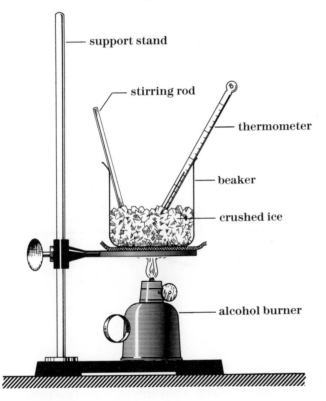

Procedure

1. Predict what will happen to the temperature of the ice as
   it melts.
2. Prepare a table for your observations like the following
   one.

Time (min)	Temperature (°C)	Notes
0.5		
1.0		
1.5		

3. Put about 200 mL of crushed ice into the beaker. Place the thermometer in the beaker so that its bulb is in the centre of the ice.

4. Observe and record the temperature once it has become steady and constant.

5. Gently heat the beaker of ice. Stir the ice occasionally.

6. Observe the temperature of the ice 30 s after you begin to heat the ice. Keeping the ice well stirred, continue to record its temperature at 30-s intervals. Keep recording temperatures up to 5 min after all the ice has melted. Also note what you see happening in the beaker, and record these observations in the *Notes* column. Be certain to note the temperature at which the ice begins to melt.

7. Prepare axes for a graph that will show ice temperature at various times. Set up the axes as shown in this graph.

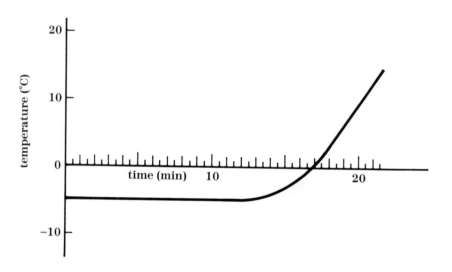

8. Plot your readings of temperature against time. For example, to record your first reading, find the spot on the temperature axis that represents the temperature of the first reading. Then mark an × at that spot, directly above 0.5 on the time axis.

9. Make a line graph by drawing a smooth curve that will join as many × marks as possible. Look at the example of a curve in the graph.

Discussion

Melting ice floes in Canada's North

1. Compare the shape of your graph with the graph on page 116.
2. Examine your graph. Describe how the temperature behaves **a)** during melting and **b)** after melting.
3. Note the temperature range at which the water is **a)** only a solid, **b)** both a solid and a liquid, and **c)** only a liquid.
4. Compare your results with your predictions. How well did you predict the way the temperature would change?
5. What is the melting point of ice?
6. Do you think other materials have the same melting point as ice? Explain.
7. In order to melt ice, do you need to add heat or remove it?

Extension

1. Repeat Activity 2 using **a)** ice made from water with salt dissolved in it, and **b)** paraffin instead of ice. After heating the paraffin, allow it to cool, and continue recording its temperature. *Caution: Paraffin is flammable at high temperatures. Check with your teacher before doing this activity.*

Heating Water

ACTIVITY 3

In this activity, you will again be observing and recording temperatures. This time, you will be heating water in the liquid state and observing its behavior.

Materials

250-mL beaker half filled with water
foil pie plate
thermometer
support stand and clamp
large beaker
alcohol burner (or other source of heat)

Warm temperatures and a lack of rain caused this stream bed to dry up.

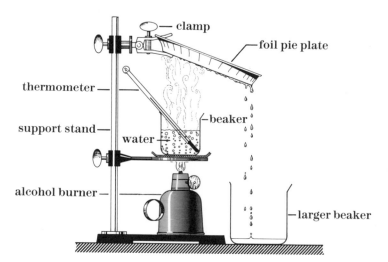

Procedure

1. Record the volume of water in the beaker.
2. Heat the water. Observe its temperature every 30 s. Record your temperature readings and other observations in a table similar to the one in Activity 2. Be certain to note the exact temperature at which any changes occur.
3. Clamp the foil pie plate above the beaker as shown. Observe and collect in the large beaker any substance produced.
4. Continue heating the water for 5 min.
5. Remove the heat source. When the beaker is cool enough to touch, record the volume of the water.
6. Plot your readings of temperature against time.

Discussion

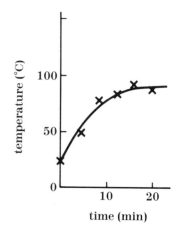

1. Did the volume of the water increase or decrease as it was heated?
2. During what period of time did the volume change most rapidly?
3. How could you explain the change in the volume of water? How did your observations of the bottom of the pie plate support this inference?
4. At what temperature did the most noticeable change to the water occur?
5. Did any of the water change into vapor at temperatures lower than the temperature you identified in question 4?
6. In order to change water into vapor, is heat added to the water or taken away?
7. In order to change water vapor into liquid water, is heat added to the water vapor or taken away?

Defining Changes of State

Substances change state only under certain conditions. For example, in Activity 2 you saw that if ice at 0°C is heated, it changes from a solid to a liquid in a process called melting.

If water at 0°C is cooled, it changes from a liquid to a solid. This process is called **solidification**, or sometimes **freezing**. Solidification is the reverse of melting. Melting and solidification occur at a temperature that is a characteristic property of any substance. This temperature is called the **melting point** of a substance. The melting point of water is 0°C.

In Activity 3, you saw that if water is heated to 100°C, it changes from a liquid to a gas. This process is called **vaporization**, or sometimes **boiling**.

If water vapor at 100°C is cooled, it changes from a gas to a liquid. This process is called **condensation**. Condensation is the reverse of vaporization. The temperature at which vaporization and condensation occur is called the **boiling point** of a substance. The boiling point is also a characteristic property of a substance. The boiling point of water is 100°C. Liquids also change to gas at temperatures below their boiling point. However, this is a very slow process. For example, water in a glass at 20°C will eventually become vapor and disappear. This process is called **evaporation**.

In general, when most substances are heated they first change from solids to liquids at their melting points. Then they change from liquids to gases at their boiling points. Under some conditions certain substances change directly from solids to gases. This process is called **sublimation**. The reverse process, the change from a gas to a solid, is also called sublimation. As an example, snow can disappear on days

Early morning dew (*left*) is the result of condensation. The frost on the windowpane (*right*) is the result of sublimation.

Dry ice sublimates to a gas to produce "smoke" for a rock concert.

when the temperature is well below 0°C. The snow is changing directly to water vapor. On the same kinds of days, ice crystals can appear in the air. Water vapor is changing directly to a solid.

When a substance changes state, it either gives off or absorbs heat energy. For example, an ice cube placed in a soft drink will absorb heat energy from the surrounding liquid. This heat energy causes the ice cube to melt. The soft drink becomes colder because it gives heat energy to the ice cube. The heat energy lost by the soft drink is gained by the ice cube. The ice cube melting in the soft drink represents a change from a solid state to a liquid state.

On the other hand, suppose water is put into an ice cube tray and then placed in a freezer. This water will eventually turn into ice. In other words, it will change from a liquid state to a solid state. This change happens when the heat energy in the water is released. This heat energy is eventually pumped out of the refrigerator.

The blue arrows in this diagram indicate changes of state in which energy is absorbed, while red arrows indicate changes in which energy is released.

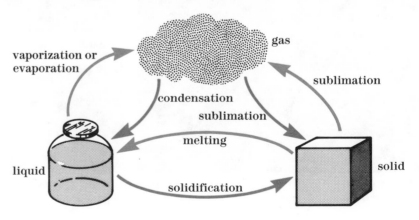

Questions

1. Identify the change of state illustrated by each of the following examples. Which objects in the pictures are absorbing heat? Which objects are releasing heat?

a) Sunbathers

b) Lava

c) Clouds

d) Drying fish

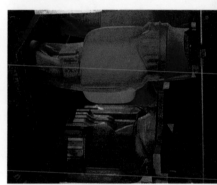

e) Plastic moulding

2. List five cooking ingredients that change state while being cooked.

3. Dehumidifiers are used to reduce the amount of water vapor in the air within houses and other buildings. How do they collect the water vapor?

4. Even on a warm summer day, you may feel cool if you do not dry yourself off after swimming. What happens to the water on your body? What change of state is involved? Why does this cool you off?

5. Why is ice at 0°C more effective for cooling a drink than the same amount of water at 0°C?

6. In a frost-free refrigerator, ice is removed by a fan that drives water vapor out of the inside of the freezer compartment. What change of state is involved? Does this change of state help or hinder the cooling of the contents of the refrigerator? What does this do to ice cubes?

7. How do hair dryers dry hair? Does your hair reach the boiling point of water when it dries?

8. Sketch a temperature-time graph for a sample of water as it is heated from −50°C to 150°C. Mark clearly on your sketch the freezing and boiling points of water, along with the periods when the sample is **a)** a solid, **b)** a liquid, **c)** a gas, **d)** a solid and a liquid, and **e)** a liquid and a gas.

5.4

Using Changes of State to Identify Substances

You can describe substances by investigating their properties. In Activities 2 and 3, you found the boiling and melting points of water. From Activity 1, you know that paraffin has its own melting point even though you did not measure it. From these activities you can see that all substances do not have the same melting point.

The properties of many substances are known and recorded. For example, the table below lists the melting and boiling points of some common substances.

Substance	Melting Point (°C)	Boiling Point (°C)
water	0	100
paraffin	55	—
ethyl alcohol	−117	78
methyl alcohol	−97	65
mercury	−39	357
nitrogen	−210	−196

You can use the information in a table like this to work backward. That is, you can determine properties of an unknown substance to infer the identity of the substance. The more properties you examine, the more certain you can be about your inference.

Sugar starts to break down at a temperature just slightly above its melting point. When it does this it produces the caramel that you see on this dessert.

Determining the Identity of a Liquid

In this activity, you will identify a liquid by finding its boiling point.

Materials

clear, colorless liquid (supplied by your teacher)
test tube
beaker
thermometer
electric kettle (or other source of boiling water)

The planet Mars is much colder than Earth, especially in the polar regions. Mars has polar ice caps like Earth, but they are not made only of frozen water. Winter temperatures in the polar regions of Mars are so cold that carbon dioxide gas in the atmosphere condenses and crystallizes on the surface like a fine, dust-like snow. These carbon dioxide frosts can form thin, temporary ice caps, covering vast regions beyond the water ice caps.

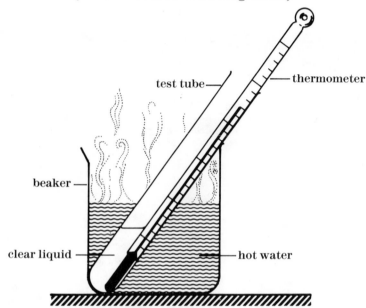

Procedure

1. Pour about 10 mL of the colorless liquid into the test tube and place the thermometer in the liquid.
2. Fill the beaker two thirds full of boiling water. Stand the test tube of liquid in this hot water bath.
3. Find the boiling point of the liquid.
   Caution: This liquid may be flammable. Keep it away from any open flame.

Discussion

1. Examine the table on page 122. What substance do you think the liquid is?
2. What could you do to become more certain of your identification of the liquid?

Weather and Climate

People always seem to be talking about the weather. Weather affects how you dress and whether or not you travel in a car, boat, or plane. Many scientists also feel that weather conditions affect your body, influencing your moods and behavior.

Many factors influence the weather, making weather forecasting an extremely complex task. In Canada, weather forecasts are provided by the Atmospheric Environment Service (AES). To make forecasts, scientists at the AES need to make observations of the atmosphere. Some observations are collected by satellites. Many other observations are made by several thousand volunteers located across Canada.

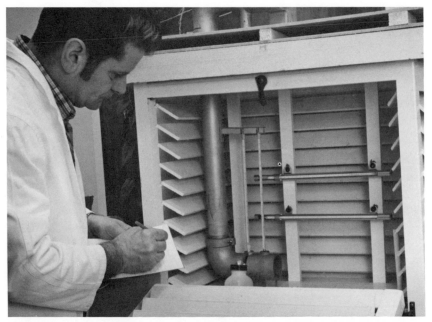

Weather forecasting is made possible by the collection of data by the Atmospheric Environment Service.

Because so much information is needed, the AES uses a supercomputer to analyse information. The CRAY supercomputer in Montreal is one of a handful of computers around the world known as "number crunchers." These are powerful computers capable of performing a vast number of calculations very quickly. The CRAY computer produces future possible weather patterns that are used by regional offices to produce more detailed forecasts.

For most people, knowledge of weather conditions is very convenient. However, for many people like fishermen and farmers and for industries like airline or power companies, knowledge of weather conditions is essential, for safety as well as for economic reasons.

Over short periods of time, weather seems unpredictable. Over long periods of time, patterns and trends become evident to the weather experts. These patterns of atmospheric conditions are known as climate.

Atmospheric conditions are a global concern for scientists. For example, scientists have been studying the problem of acid rain for several decades. Their research has shown that pollutants causing acid rain often originate several hundred miles from the location of acid rain-damaged areas.

Another pollution problem that has come to light since the late 1970s is arctic haze. During the winter months, suspended particles of pollutants in the arctic air increase to roughly one-tenth of their concentration in eastern North America. Scientists think that this level of pollution is increasing. Most of the pollution comes from Europe, northern Asia, and eastern North America. Scientists at the AES have developed an instrument called a sunphotometer that measures intensity of sunlight. This instrument was tested in space by Dr. Marc Garneau and is valuable in studying arctic haze.

Scientists at the AES are studying many aspects of the environment. Their research projects include the study of the long-range movement of pollutants, such as carbon dioxide and ozone, drought, and climate changes such as possible global warming or cooling. They share their information with scientists around the world. This research results in a better understanding of the atmosphere and an increasing knowledge of how to prevent problems.

Accurate weather forecasts are very important in many situations.

Connections

Increasing the Certainty

The measurement of one property allows you to infer what a substance is. When you measure several properties, you increase the certainty of the inference. Two substances may have the same melting points. However, there is less chance that both substances have the same melting points and the same boiling points. In Activity 5, you will examine the original problem of checking to see if water is a major component of tomato juice.

ACTIVITY 5   Examining Tomato Juice

Does tomato juice contain water? If it does, you should be able to heat the juice until the water boils, and be able to collect the water vapor. This is an example of a process called **distillation**. In this activity, you will collect the gas and cool it in a test tube. Then, you will do some tests on the liquid to see if it is water.

Materials

tomato juice
flask
boiling chips
one-hole rubber stopper
adjustable clamp
ring stand, iron ring, wire gauze
glass tubing
test tubes
large beaker
alcohol burner (or other source of heat)
safety goggles
thermometer
salt
crushed ice

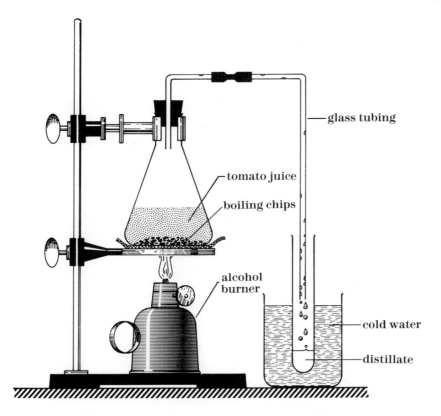

- glass tubing
- tomato juice
- boiling chips
- alcohol burner
- cold water
- distillate

During the warm days of spring and fall, it would be impossible to play hockey without artificial ice. When temperatures are too high for natural ice, a rink's surface can be kept frozen by using salt water as an antifreeze. Salt water can be cooled below the freezing point of ordinary water. The cold salt water is circulated in pipes below the ice surface. Because the salt water is colder than the ice, it draws heat from the ice and keeps it from melting.

Procedure

Part A: Distillation

1. Set up the apparatus as shown. Place 90 mL of tomato juice and some boiling chips in the flask. Be certain that the stopper is inserted firmly into the flask.
2. Heat the tomato juice slowly, so that it just boils.
3. Continue heating until you have collected three test tubes of liquid.
4. Describe the liquid you have collected.

Part B: Identification

1. Find the boiling point of the liquid you have collected. To do this, heat one test tube of the liquid and measure the temperature when it starts to boil.
2. Find the freezing point of the liquid. To do this, place a mixture of crushed ice and salt in a beaker. Insert one test tube of the liquid into this mixture. Measure the temperature when the liquid freezes.
3. Present your conclusion of the identity of the liquid. Give your evidence for this conclusion.

Extension

1. Is there any other test that might confirm the identity of the liquid? If there is, check with your teacher and, if possible, perform it.
2. Repeat Activity 5 using several different brands of tomato juice. You can also use other kinds of juices.
3. Devise a test to determine the amount of water in a fresh tomato.

Questions

1. Both ethyl alcohol and methyl alcohol are clear, colorless liquids. Methyl alcohol, however, is highly poisonous. How might you be able to identify methyl alcohol?
2. A white solid is heated and its melting point is determined to be 55°C. What might this substance be? How could you test your conclusions further?

Case Study

Refining Petroleum

Oil rigs are used to bring oil up from under the ocean.

Petroleum or crude oil is one of Canada's most important resources. One reason for its importance is that it consists of so many different substances. These substances are identified and separated primarily by means of their different boiling points.

The petroleum that comes out of the ground is a black, sticky liquid. It is a mixture of thousands of different substances. Some petrochemical products consist of single substances like propane and butane, while others, like gasoline, are mixtures of several substances. Here is a table listing some of the substances in petroleum.

Substance	Melting Point (°C)	Boiling Point (°C)	Uses
methane	−182.5	−161	home heating fuel
propane	−190	−43	portable bottle fuel
butane	−138	−0.5	lighter fluid
octane	−57	125	gasoline
tridecane	−5.5	236	kerosene
pentadecane	10	271	fuel oil
oils		>300	lubricating oils
paraffin	55	>350	candles

Petroleum is separated into various components by distillation in a device called a *bubble tower*. The bubble tower consists of 20 to 30 trays arranged vertically about 75 cm apart. The petroleum is heated to 370°C and pumped into the tower near the bottom. Most of the petroleum vaporizes immediately. The vapor rises through openings in the trays called bubbles. The vapor continues to rise until each component reaches a tray with a temperature low enough to allow the component to condense. In this way, the substances with higher boiling points condense near the bottom of the tower

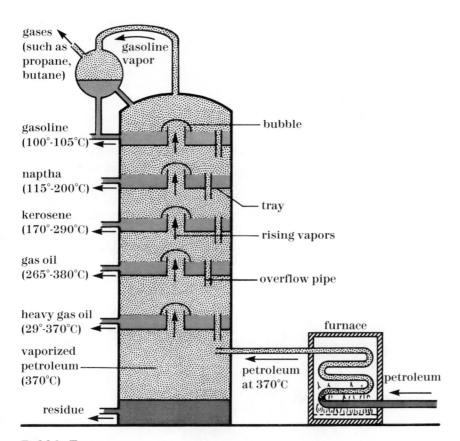

Bubble Tower

and are removed from the vapor. Substances with lower boiling points condense further up the tower. Most of the time, the substances are removed from the tower in mixtures that have similar boiling points. Gasoline, fuel oil, and kerosene are some of the more common mixtures.

1. While the primary use for petroleum is as a fuel, it is also used to manufacture many different products from plastics to medicines. List at least five products made from petroleum.

2. Look at the substances in the table on page 128. Which of these are liquids at room temperature (20°C)? Which are gases? Are any of them solids?

3. Why must propane be stored in a high-pressure gas bottle until it is used?

Biography

Abraham Gesner

The discovery of kerosene made possible a brighter, safer source of light than candles.

Abraham Gesner was born near Cornwallis, Nova Scotia, in 1797. At that time, the most common sources of heat and light were wood fires and candles. Over the decades that followed, Gesner brought about a major change in household energy sources.

After finishing his basic schooling in Nova Scotia, Gesner spent a few years in London, England, where he trained as a doctor. Returning to Nova Scotia in the late 1820s, he began a medical practice. By the late 1830s, he had moved to Saint John, New Brunswick, to work as a geologist.

Abraham Gesner
Discoverer of kerosene

While on a geological survey in southeastern New Brunswick, he observed deposits of a dark, tarry material among rock formations. It was known that this material, called *bitumen*, could be burned as a fuel. Gesner decided to do some experiments in distilling bitumen, thinking that it might be more useful in a more refined form. By the time he returned to Nova Scotia at the age of forty-six, he knew he had found something worth investigating.

After ten more years of careful tests, he perfected the process of distilling a yellowish oil from the natural bitumen tar. He called his discovery kerosene, from the Greek word for wax. The name was well chosen because kerosene lamps were soon to become the standard replacement for wax candles. Under his direction, a factory on Long Island, New York, was built to refine bitumen into kerosene. At the age of sixty-six, the successful inventor was appointed as a professor at Dalhousie University in Halifax.

Today, kerosene is still used as a fuel for portable heaters and as a fuel for jet aircraft. Gesner also invented one of the first useful wood preservatives, a road-paving process, and a way of making charcoal briquettes from coal dust.

Abraham Gesner also invented a process for producing charcoal briquettes, shown here on a modern production line.

Summary

Changes in matter involve changes in the properties of matter. These changes are called chemical changes when a new substance is produced, and physical changes when no new substance is produced.

Many substances can exist in any of three physical states as solids, liquids, or gases, depending upon conditions.

There are six changes of state. Condensation and freezing both give off heat. Evaporation and melting both absorb heat.

The shiny surfaces of a car dashboard are produced by sublimating a thin coating of aluminum onto plastic parts.

There are two kinds of sublimation. In the change of a gas to a solid, heat is given off. In the change of a solid to a gas, heat is absorbed.

Matter can change physically from one state to another. The six changes of state are summarized in this table.

Change of State	Before	After
vaporization*	liquid	gas
condensation	gas	liquid
solidification	liquid	solid
melting	solid	liquid
sublimation	solid	gas
sublimation	gas	solid

*Evaporation is a change from a liquid to a gas below the boiling point of a substance.

At high altitudes, campers find that water boils at a lower temperature.

Vaporization and condensation usually occur at a specific temperature for a given substance. This temperature is called the boiling point of the substance. The temperature at which solidification and melting take place is the melting point of a substance. The melting and boiling points of a sample of material are useful in establishing the identity of the substance. Changes of state can also be used to separate the components of a mixture of substances.

Chapter Questions

Remember

1. Classify the following as physical or chemical changes.
   a) condensation of water on a car windshield
   b) cooking a hot dog
   c) sawing a piece of wood
   d) digesting food
   e) melting ice
2. Which of these statements are true? false? Rewrite the false statements to make them true.
   a) Liquids have neither a fixed volume nor a fixed shape.

b) Gases have neither a fixed volume nor a fixed shape.

c) A change of state from a solid to a gas is known as condensation.

d) A change of state from a liquid to a solid is known as freezing.

e) During evaporation heat is given off.

f) During freezing heat is given off.

3. What enables the components of petroleum to be separated during distillation?

Think

1. Why do aerosol spray cans cool down when you use them?

2. Refrigerators often use changes of state between Freon gas and liquid Freon. Which change of state produces the cooling? What does the other change of state do?

3. Sketch a temperature-time graph for a sample of mercury heated from −100°C to 500°C. Identify the different changes of state of the mercury as it is heated, and record the temperature at which each change takes place.

4. Make a poster to display some uses of changes of state in the world around you.

5. a) What change of state is occurring when a solid air freshener fills a room with scent?

   b) What happens to the size of the block of air freshener?

6. Examine the top of an ice cube tray filled with ice cubes. Does the surface of the ice cube bulge upward or downward? Does water expand or contract when it freezes?

7. The freezing point of water can be reduced by the addition of antifreeze. Check a can of antifreeze to find the following.

   a) How low can the antifreeze reduce the freezing point of water?

   b) What concentration of antifreeze in water gives the best protection (the lowest freezing point)?

Divers have to take tanks of compressed air underwater with them in order to breathe.

Dream

1. The human body contains solids. liquids, and gases. Name some substances in your body that are solids. Why is it important that they are solids? Do the same for bodily substances that are a) liquids and b) gases.

2. Liquids do not have fixed shapes. Gases have neither a fixed shape nor a fixed volume. In what ways could these properties be useful? Give examples.

3. Construct a model of an apparatus resembling a bubble tower to separate the various components of an imaginary new material, called *pebblonium*, brought back from Jupiter.

Decide

1. Mercury was commonly used in the construction of thermometers. Mercury, however, is very poisonous. Its low boiling point causes it to evaporate quite easily, after which it spreads through the atmosphere.
   a) What substances have been found as substitutes for mercury?
   b) What safety precautions are necessary if mercury needs to be used?
2. Methyl alcohol is very poisonous. It is used in some kinds of duplicating machines. Even when methyl alcohol is kept away from young children, there is still concern over its use in schools.
   a) Why does this concern exist?
   b) What precautions are necessary if methyl alcohol is used in schools?

6

Chemical Change

Investigators use many kinds of tools and techniques to help them to discover facts. Fingerprint investigators, often involved in police work, can make fingerprints appear by dusting a surface with powder. They also can use a technique involving lasers that was pioneered in Canada. The laser light reacts with substances in finger secretions, which makes the fingerprints glow. Forensic analysts also are investigators who often help the police to discover or prove facts. Most forensic analysts investigate substances to identify them.

Other kinds of investigators also need to identify substances. Environmental analysts try to determine what pollutants exist in air, water, or soil. Geochemists identify the substances in rocks. Quality control technologists identify the substances in manufactured products such as food or cosmetics.

How do these investigators identify substances?

It is often difficult to tell one substance from another by looking at them. For example, there are many white powders that could be mistaken for coffee whitener. To solve the problem of identifying coffee whitener, you could use trial and error. Imagine, however, what your family would say if you used powdered detergent instead of coffee whitener. To solve problems like this you will find it helpful to combine information about substances with problem-solving strategies.

6.1

Identifying Substances by Chemical Changes

Many clear, colorless liquids can easily be mistaken for water. Some of these liquids, methyl alcohol, for example, are poisonous. How could you safely identify different substances that look the same. In chapter 5 you used physical changes to describe and identify some of these substances.

You can also describe and identify substances in another way that is especially useful when you have several substances that look similar. You can determine what each substance will do when it is mixed with other substances. When you do this, you are investigating chemical changes. In chapter 5 you learned that a chemical change is any change to a substance that produces another substance. The study of chemical changes is called **chemistry**.

In the same way that every substance has a set of characteristic physical changes and properties, every substance also has

A chemical change can often be identified by a change of color. To produce the pink-red solid on the right, the green nickel solution was combined with the clear, colorless dimethyl glyoxine solution.

a set of characteristic chemical changes and properties. For example, both dish detergent and egg white produce foam. How can you tell them apart? You might try heating them. When you heat egg white in a frying pan or in the oven, new substances are produced, that is, a chemical change occurs. If you do the same thing with dish detergent, you only get hot detergent. No chemical change occurs. These characteristics can be used to tell the difference between foam from egg whites and foam from dish detergent.

There are many chemical properties that have been investigated and recorded for many known substances. In this chapter, you will use some of this knowledge to perform **chemical tests** to identify unknown substances. You will also investigate the properties of some special groups of substances.

Gathering Evidence

If you want to identify unknown substances in your kitchen, you can observe their properties. In this activity, you will examine a number of white powders.

Materials

sheet of wax paper
five white powders
hand lens or microscope and slides

Procedure

1. Make a full-page table like the one below.

	Powder				
	1	2	3	4	5
Properties					
smell					
particle shape					
color					
other					
Identification					
your prediction					
your reasons					

Specially dressed employees of a Halifax environment clean-up company shovel soil contaminated by poisonous organic compounds into bags.

2. Make five circles on the sheet of wax paper. Number the circles 1 to 5 and place one spoonful of each of the powders in the appropriate circle.

3. Examine each of the powders using your senses of sight, touch, and smell. Record your observations. *Do not taste unknown substances. They could be poisonous or hazardous.*

4. Using a hand lens or a microscope, look more closely at the particles of the powders. Use the low-power objective lens on the microscope. Record your observations of particle shape in your table.

5. Guess and record what you think each of the powders might be. Record the reasons for your guess.

Discussion

1. Which powders were the most alike? What are some tests you might do to tell them apart more easily?

2. Why is it unsafe to use a taste test with unknown substances in the laboratory?

ACTIVITY 2

The process of baking a cake involves chemical changes.

Observing Chemical Behaviour

In this activity, you will perform four tests on each of the five powders from Activity 1. These tests will allow you to observe and compare how each powder behaves when it is mixed with other substances and when it is heated.

Materials

sheet of wax paper
five white powders
hand lens or microscope and slides
water
vinegar
iodine solution
3 eyedroppers
stirrers
test tubes
alcohol burner or other source of heat
fireproof pad
aluminum foil cups
safety goggles
pair of tongs or oven gloves

Procedure

1. Make a full-page table like the one below.

Test	Powder				
	1	2	3	4	5
water					
vinegar					
iodine					
heat					

2. Repeat step 2 from Activity 1.
3. With the eyedropper, add a few drops of water to each powder separately and stir gently.
4. Record your observations for each of the five powders.
5. Number the test tubes from 1 to 5.
6. Put a small, level spoonful of the first powder into the first test tube. Match up the other substances in the same way. Each test tube should contain the same amount of powder.
7. Fill the first test tube with water and shake it vigorously for a moment or two. Do the same with the other test tubes.
8. Once each test tube has stood for at least 1 min, observe and record any changes.
9. Using vinegar instead of water, repeat steps 2 through 8.
10. Using iodine instead of water, repeat steps 2 through 4. *Handle the iodine solution with care.* Iodine will stain skin, clothing, and desk tops.
11. Put a small, level spoonful of each powder in a separate aluminum foil cup. Hold each cup with a pair of tongs or gloves and heat the cup over the alcohol burner for about 1 min. *Wear safety goggles to reduce the risk that the heated material will splatter into your eyes.*
12. As each powder is heated, record your observations.

Discussion

1. Which powder could you separate from all of the others using each of these tests by itself?
   a) the water test
   c) the iodine test
   b) the vinegar test
   d) the heat test
2. Which substances dissolved in water?

3. Which substances melted when heated? What could you infer about the melting points of the other substances? Would all of the powders melt if the temperature were high enough? What might happen before they melted?

4. Was a new substance produced in any of the tests? If so, in which test? What do you think the substance was?

6.2

Useful Properties for Identification

Structure

Structure is a property of a solid substance. In Activity 1, you may have noticed two kinds of structure.

Some substances, such as salt and sugar, are particles that all have the same shape. Such particles are called **crystals**. The substances are called **crystalline substances**. Even if the particles of crystalline substances have different sizes, they have the same shape.

Some materials do not have a characteristic crystalline shape, but are particles of all shapes. Plaster of Paris and starch are examples of substances that are not made of crystals. Such substances are called **non-crystalline substances**.

a) Copper sulphate

b) Azurite malachite

c) Galena

d) Pectolite

e) Fluorite

f) Chalcedony

Materials with differently shaped crystals

Solvents and Solutions

Sugar, salt, and baking soda seem to disappear when mixed with water. In other words, they **dissolve**. A substance that can dissolve other substances is a **solvent**. A solvent with one or more substances dissolved in it is a **solution**. When the liquid part of a solution disappears, the dissolved substances reappear. For example, if a solution of water and sugar were allowed to evaporate, the sugar would be left behind. This shows that the sugar has not been turned into a new substance. Therefore, the ability to dissolve is a physical property, not a chemical property.

Water is the most common solvent, but some materials also dissolve in other solvents. Other common solvents are methyl alcohol, ethyl alcohol, kerosene, and gasoline. Two common powders, cornstarch and plaster of Paris, do not dissolve in water.

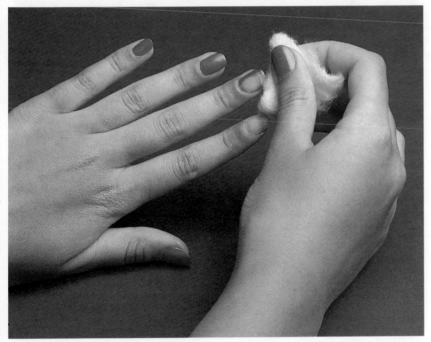

Nail polish remover is a solvent that dissolves nail polish.

Chemical Changes

Some combinations of substances produce gas bubbles. Baking soda when mixed with vinegar produces carbon dioxide

When beer is brewed in these large vats, carbon dioxide gas is produced.

gas. The gas formed is a new substance. In chapter 5 you learned that this kind of event is called a chemical change. In a chemical change, new matter is created from old. A chemical change can be represented by a chemical word equation. The reaction between baking soda and vinegar can be represented by this equation.

$$\text{vinegar} + \text{baking soda} \longrightarrow \text{carbon dioxide gas} + \text{other substances}$$

You might have observed in Activity 2 that plaster of Paris changes when combined with water. This reaction is also a chemical change and can be represented by this equation.

$$\text{plaster of Paris powder} + \text{water} \longrightarrow \text{hydrated plaster of Paris (hard solid)}$$

The dark blue color produced when the iodine solution was added to a substance containing starch is a chemical change. Iodine does not produce this characteristic color when added to any of the other white powders or substances not containing starch. The reaction between iodine and starch could be shown in the following equation.

$$\text{iodine} + \text{cornstarch} \longrightarrow \text{dark blue substance}$$

Heat can cause some materials to change. Wood contains substances called hydrocarbons which burn when heated enough in the presence of oxygen. This is the word equation for burning.

$$\text{oxygen in air} + \text{hydrocarbons in wood} \longrightarrow \text{carbon dioxide gas} + \text{water vapor} + \text{other substances}$$

Substances like sugar and starch do not burn but decompose when heated. The sugar melts before it starts to decompose. The result is a dark brown substance, called caramel, which contains carbon.

$$\text{heat} + \text{sugar} \longrightarrow \text{carbon} + \text{water vapor} + \text{other substances}$$

Salt does not appear to change at all when heated.

Considering the Evidence

ACTIVITY 3

In this activity, you will weigh the evidence that you gathered in Activity 2 to identify each of the five powders.

Materials

record of observations from Activities 1 and 2

Procedure

1. Prepare a summary of the properties or tests you could use to distinguish each of the five powders used in Activities 1 and 2. Use what you have just read about each powder to make a prediction about its structure and its behavior during a water test and a heat test.
2. Organize the information from step 1 in a table like the one on page 146. Salt is already done as an example. In a similar way, record your information for each of the other four substances: cornstarch, plaster of Paris, baking soda, and sugar. You may want to choose different tests or properties for these substances.

Powder	Property or Test	Expected Observation
salt	structure	crystalline
	water test	salt dissolves
	iodine test	no change
	vinegar test	no change
	heat test	no change

3. Compare your observations for each of the five powders in Activities 1 and 2 with the predictions for this activity. Identify each of the five unknown powders by matching each with one of the substances named in the chart.

Discussion

1. Which of the tests you did and properties you examined were most useful for identifying each powder? Underline the most useful test for each powder in your table.

Extension

1. Try to find some other materials that are crystalline. You may need to use a hand lens or microscope to help you.
2. Add some lemon juice to baking soda. What do you observe? What might you conclude?
3. a) Dissolve two spoonfuls of salt in half a glass of water. Then taste the water. *Remember you never taste substances unless you know that they are safe.* Why might you think that the salt is still in the water?
   b) Using sugar instead of salt, repeat part a).
   c) Were the changes in parts a) and b) physical changes or chemical changes? Why?
4. Place some baking soda in a balloon, and some vinegar in a pill vial. Stretch the open end of the balloon over the end of the vial, and then dump the baking soda into the vinegar. Observe the results. Write a chemical word equation to express the results.

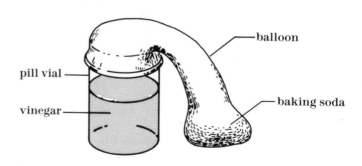

Using Chemistry to Solve Problems

One of the uses of chemistry is to classify and identify different substances. These can be **natural substances**, or **synthetic substances**. Synthetic substances are made from other substances in a laboratory. How can you use your knowledge of chemistry to classify and identify substances? You can use the properties of a substance. As an example, you have observed that table salt consists of small, cube-shaped particles. Salt dissolves in water, vinegar, and iodine solutions without producing a new substance. It remains unchanged by heating. But many other substances have some or all of these same properties.

Suppose you had to find out which substance in a group of unknown substances was coffee whitener. You could begin by reviewing the four steps of the problem-solving model in chapter 1 on page 5.

The *definition of the problem* can be posed as a question. Which of the unknown substances had the same properties as coffee whitener? You must, therefore, consider the properties of coffee whitener. What is its texture? What happens when it is combined with a solvent?

The *suggestion of several possible solutions* can be done by testing the unknown substances, then observing and recording the properties of each substance.

The *consideration of each possible solution* will involve a comparison of the properties of each unknown substance with the properties of coffee whitener. Where there are differences, reject the unknown solutions.

The *choice of one solution* will be made once you discover which unknown substance has exactly the same properties as coffee whitener.

One possible solution to the problems caused by acid rain is the addition of lime to affected lakes, which is shown here being done by airplane.

ACTIVITY 4

Identifying Coffee Whitener

In this activity, you will identify coffee whitener from a group of unidentified kitchen substances. To do so, you will use the four-step problem-solving model.

Materials

Milk and orange juice both contain very important chemical nutrients. Milk contains calcium, which is used by your body for the growth and maintenance of teeth and bones. The vitamin C found in orange juice is also vital to good health. Skin and other body tissues need vitamin C for the repair of cuts, bruises, and other damage.

sheet of wax paper
coffee whitener
unlabelled edible white powders
hand lens or microscope and slides
water
vinegar
iodine solution
3 eyedroppers
stirrers
test tubes
alcohol burner or other source of heat
fireproof pad
aluminum foil cups
safety goggles
pair of tongs or oven gloves

Procedure

Part A: Definition of the Problem

1. Examine a sample of coffee whitener and record its physical properties: color, smell, appearance, structure.
2. Test the whitener using the tests from Activities 1 and 2 on pages 139-42. Record your observations.

Part B: Suggestion of Several Possible Solutions

1. Devise other tests that you think would be useful to distinguish the coffee whitener from the other substances. Be sure that you have the proper materials and use the appropriate safety precautions. If necessary, check each test with your teacher before trying it. For example, never use a taste test for any substance in class unless you are assured by your teacher that it is safe.
2. Perform your tests. Record your observations for each test.

Part C: Consideration of Each Possible Solution

1. Plan how you will identify which of the unknown substances is the coffee whitener. Check your plan with your teacher and change it if necessary.

2. Follow your plan to identify the coffee whitener from the other kitchen chemicals. Record your observations for each step in your plan.

Part D: Choice of One Solution
1. Review your observations. Identify the unknown substance that has exactly the same properties as coffee whitener.

Discussion

1. Could you have changed the order of the steps in your plan to save time? If so, how? Which steps could you have left out?
2. What are some other properties of substances that could have been observed, but were not, because of limitations in materials?

Extension

1. Many of the products used as substitutes for natural foods are synthetic. The problem is to find an acceptable combination of chemicals that will perform the same function as the food they replace. Examine the list of ingredients in coffee whitener. Which ingredients come from a cow?
2. Obtain samples of various products used to whiten coffee. Compare the following.
   a) ingredients
   b) expected shelf life
   c) nutritional value
   d) behavior when mixed with hot water
   e) taste (You can assume that these products are safe as they are all edible products.)
   f) cost
3. Do a comparison of natural and artificial sweeteners. Which are the most desirable? Why?
4. Obtain a sample that is an unknown mixture of two or more of the white powders used in Activity 1. Devise a way to identify the different powders in the mixtures.

To unclog a kitchen sink drain, you might use a chemical drain cleaner. These cleaners are usually strong bases. The clog consists mainly of animal and vegetable matter that is decomposed by strong bases. Like a detergent, the drain cleaner also breaks down the fatty substances in the clog. The drain cleaner, however, is much stronger chemically than the detergent.

Problem Solving for Consumers

If you are shopping for kitchen products, you have to make choices. Labels and advertisements present information

Product packages can be informative as well as attractive.

designed to convince you that the products are your best possible choice.

Would you choose the product that presents the best image or the one that is most popular with your friends? Smart shoppers spend time investigating before they buy. How can you select the product that will give you the most value for your money? To make this selection, you can use the four-step problem-solving model. You probably would not conduct your tests quite so formally or in a laboratory. But you can gather evidence about properties of different products, compare them and select the best one.

All processed and packaged food products must indicate the ingredients on their labels. This list is an important source of information for consumers. It shows everything contained in the product in order from the highest to the lowest percentage of the product's total mass. In some cases, such as cereal boxes, the actual masses of the different ingredients are shown. Label reading is one way of gathering evidence.

Labels provide important information about a product's ingredients.

Acid rain, acid stomach, acid soil, and acid spills are terms with which you might be familiar. **Acidity** is one of the properties used to classify substances. Substances are either **acid**, **base**, or **neutral** (neither acid nor base).

6.4

Acid or Not

Acids Can Be Useful The acid in gastric fluid digests food	➤	**So Can Bases** Mild bases are used to soothe upset stomachs
Acids Can Be Tasty Mild acids can add flavor to foods, such as vinegar and lemon juice in salad dressings	➤	**Bases Never Can** Bases in foods and medicines give them a bitter taste
Acids Can Be Harmful Some soft drinks are so acidic that they can dissolve tooth enamel	➤	**So Can Bases** Oven cleaners can corrode unenamelled metal surfaces

Some tests have been designed to identify acids and bases. Some special materials called **indicators** show whether a substance is an acid or a base.

Litmus is one such indicator. In an acid solution, red litmus stays unchanged, while blue litmus turns red. In a base solution, the opposite occurs: red litmus turns blue, while blue litmus remains unchanged. In a neutral solution, both red and blue litmus remain unchanged. **Phenolphthalein**, another indicator, is a colorless solution. When combined with a base, it turns pink. When combined with an acid or a neutral solution, it remains colorless.

ACTIVITY 5 — Testing Substances with Indicators

In this activity, you will use indicators to determine which common substances are acids and which are bases.

Materials

red and blue litmus paper
phenolphthalein solution
vinegar
lemon juice
distilled water
salt solution
ammonia water
milk
milk of magnesia powder dissolved in water
aspirin dissolved in water
tea
test tubes
straw
eyedropper

Procedure

1. Make a table like the one below.

Substance	Effect on Litmus Paper	Acid, Base or Neutral
vinegar		
lemon juice		
water		

2. Using both red and blue litmus paper, test each of the liquids. To do this, touch the paper to the surface of each liquid. *Be careful not to mix any of the liquids* together. *This may confuse your results.* Record your observations.
3. Using the phenolphthalein solution, confirm your litmus test results for vinegar, ammonia, and water. To do so, place a small sample of each liquid to be tested in a clean test tube and add a few drops of phenolphthalein.
4. Add about 1 mL of ammonia water to 1 mL of the phenolphthalein indicator. Allow the solution to turn pink.
5. Pour about 5 mL distilled water into a test tube. Add three drops of the pink phenolphthalein solution.
6. Using a straw, blow into the water until you notice a change.

Discussion

1. List separately the properties of the acids and bases you discovered in this activity.
2. In step 6, what happened when you blew into the solution? Why?

Extension

1. Use vinegar and baking soda to investigate the way in which some vegetable and fruit juices act as indicators. Some juices you can try are beet juice, red cabbage juice, cherry juice, and grape juice.
2. Use the apparatus shown in the diagram to design an experiment. In the experiment, attempt to show that ordinary air does not have the same effect as exhaled breath.

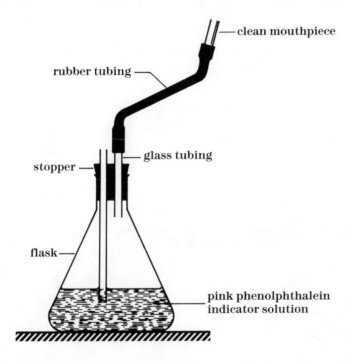

- clean mouthpiece
- rubber tubing
- glass tubing
- stopper
- flask
- pink phenolphthalein indicator solution

Acids and bases are an important part of your life. They have chemical properties that make them very useful when combined with other substances. For example, sulphuric acid is used in the manufacture of synthetic fabrics such as nylon and rayon.

Bases are useful components of medicines and cleaning materials such as detergents, but they too can be poisonous and detrimental to the environment.

Bases and acids can be used to cancel each other's effects. This reaction is called **neutralization**.

6.5

Uses of Acids and Bases

Acid Rain

Acid rain is a serious threat to the environment in many parts of Canada. It can ruin lakes and rivers, destroy forests, and damage buildings.

How is acid rain produced? Various gases in smoke and exhaust from homes, industries, and vehicles dissolve in water droplets in the atmosphere. For example, carbon dioxide gas produced by all living creatures, as well as by the burning of fuels, dissolves in water droplets, producing a weak acid called *carbonic acid*. As a result, even normal rain is slightly acidic, not neutral. Much stronger *sulphuric* and *nitrous acids* are produced in rain and snow by other kinds of dissolved gases. These gases come from the emissions of coal-burning power plants or smelters. Samples of snow and rain with a pH reading as low as 3 have been collected in parts of Canada. This kind of acid rain can dissolve minerals and damage living things.

Scientists are now collecting evidence which might prove that much of the damage seen in Canadian forests is caused by acid rainfall. It has already been proven that acid rainfall acidifies small lakes and kills or damages life in the lakes. Continued production of acid rain will change living lakes in many parts of Canada to reservoirs of crystal-clear, but lifeless, acidic water.

Coal-burning plants release polluting oxides of sulphur and nitrogen into the air.

This is an example of the way in which acid rain and soot can damage buildings.

The effect of high concentrations of these strong acids can be seen on old buildings and monuments. In Athens, Greece, the acid rain damage to the Acropolis is extensive. In Venice, Italy, the concentration of sulphuric acid in the air is sufficiently high that statues and building ornaments are being eroded. The Parliament Buildings in Ottawa also show signs of damage.

Many of these buildings have been constructed from stone such as marble and limestone. Both of these materials are forms of a mineral called calcium carbonate, which is also the main component of chalk. The acid in the rain reacts with the calcium carbonate in the building materials to cause extensive damage.

Acid rain poses complicated scientific and technological problems. Researchers must investigate and find ways to deal with both the causes and effects of acid rain. For example, scientists and technologists are trying to find practical ways to remove acid-producing materials from exhaust gases. This would reduce the production of acid rain. Scientists are also dumping neutralizing agents like calcium carbonate into lakes to reduce the acidity of the water. This helps reduce the effect of acid rain.

However, the most complicated problems posed by acid rain seem to be social and economic problems. For example, evidence indicates that major sources of acid rain are found in many countries. The politicians of these countries must cooperate to find ways to stop acid rain. This is sometimes difficult to do because the economy of many countries depends on industries that are responsible for acid rain. Because most of these industries operate to meet the needs of society, they feel it is difficult to expect them to change quickly and stay in business. For this reason, most acid rain producers feel they need more scientific evidence to prove that they are the cause of this serious problem.

1. Acid rain is slowly killing all the living creatures in many northern Canadian lakes. Suggest some possible ways to do the following.
   a) to stop the production of the acid rain
   b) to reduce the acidity of the lakes
2. How could the four-step problem-solving model be used to do the following?
   a) to identify the major sources of acid rain
   b) to identify the most effective solution(s) to the problem of acid rain

ACTIVITY 6   Investigating Acids and Bases

In this activity, you will observe chemical changes involving a variety of common materials that are either acids or bases.

Materials

vinegar
magnesium metal
chalk dust (calcium carbonate)
baking soda
milk of magnesia tablets
distilled water
lemon juice
phenolphthalein solution
red and blue litmus paper
test tubes
3 eyedroppers

Procedure

Part A: Neutralizing an Acid
1. Fill a test tube with 5 mL of vinegar. Test the vinegar with litmus paper. Add three drops of phenolphthalein solution with an eyedropper.
2. Add baking soda, a tiny bit at a time, until a color change occurs. Test the solution with litmus paper.
3. Use another eyedropper to add vinegar, one drop at a time, until the color disappears. Test the solution again with litmus paper.

Part B: Neutralizing a Base

1. Crush half a tablet of milk of magnesia and add it to 5 mL of distilled water in a test tube. Test the solution with litmus paper. Add three drops of phenolphthalein solution with an eyedropper.
2. Use an eyedropper to add lemon juice, a drop at a time, until a color change occurs. Test the solution with litmus paper.
3. Crush half a tablet of milk of magnesia and add it to the solution. Test the solution again with litmus paper.

Part C: Producing Gases

1. Put a small piece of magnesium metal into each of the test tubes used in Part A and Part B. Observe the solutions for a few minutes.
2. Using chalk instead of magnesium metal, repeat step 1.

Discussion

1. How did you neutralize the vinegar? the milk of magnesia? Was there any chemical change in either or both cases? How did you know?
2. Acids combine with some substances to produce a gas. What evidence of gas production was there in this activity?

6.6

Some Properties of Acids and Bases

In Activities 5 and 6, you were able to observe some of the properties of acids and bases. Acids turn blue litmus paper red, while bases do the opposite. Bases and acids are able to neutralize each other. Both bases and acids react chemically with certain substances.

Here are some examples of these reactions. When some metals such as magnesium are dropped into an acidic solution, hydrogen gas and a salt are produced. When chalk is dropped into an acidic solution, carbon dioxide and salt are produced. In a spacecraft, carbon dioxide is removed when it combines with the base lithium hydroxide. The products are water and the salt lithium carbonate. Some people drink sodium bicarbonate (commonly know as baking soda), dissolved in water. This base neutralizes the excess acid that causes an upset stomach.

There is another important difference that was not investigated in this activity. Acids are sour, while bases are bitter.

strong acid	0
	1
	2
	3
	4
weak acid	5
	6
neutral	7
	8
weak base	9
	10
	11
	12
strong base	13
	14

pH Scale

Measuring the Strength of Acids and Bases

Both acids and bases vary in strength. Acids and bases are classified on a quantitative scale ranging from very strong acids to very strong bases. This scale is called the **pH scale**. Strong acids have a low pH, while strong bases have a high pH. A neutral solution is assigned a pH of 7.

When an acid and a base are combined in just the right quantities, they neutralize each other, leaving a solution of salt in water.

$$\text{acid} \ + \ \text{base} \longrightarrow \text{salt} \ + \ \text{water}$$

The term salt here refers to a class of substances, many of which are used in our homes and communities. Ordinary table salt is known as *sodium chloride*. *Sodium nitrate* is a salt used to preserve meats. *Calcium chloride* is used in the summer on dirt roads to keep the dust down.

Questions

1. **a)**   List four common substances that are acids.
   b)   List four common substances that are bases.
2. What is an indicator? How do phenolphthalein solution and litmus act as indicators?
3. Write the word equations for the chemical changes produced in these reactions.
   a)   an acid is combined with metal
   b)   an acid is combined with chalk
   c)   lithium hydroxide is combined with carbon dioxide
4. Explain what it means to say that baking soda can be used to neutralize an acid?
5. *Tums* and *Rolaids* are sold as antacids.
   a)   What are they supposed to do?
   b)   What kind of substance must they contain?
   c)   What substance did you experiment with that is also sold as an antacid?

In chapter 1, you saw that the function of a particular object often depends on the properties of the substance from which it is made. This is particularly true of the class of substances called metals. If you look around you, you will see that many of the things you use everyday are made from metals. Electrical wiring is often made from copper. Machinery and tools are made primarily from iron and steel. What properties of metals make them suitable for such a variety of useful functions? How can you select the most appropriate metal for a particular function?

Metals: A Special Group of Substances

a) Mirror

b) Electrical wire

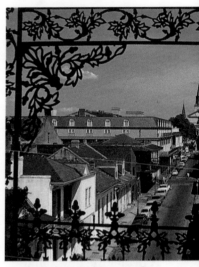

c) Ornamental wrought iron

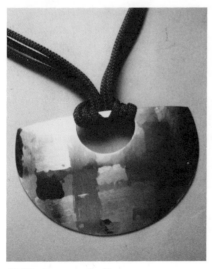

d) Hammered silver jewellery

e) Magnet

f) Coil springs

The different properties of metals make them useful for a variety of purposes. What properties of each of the above items are important for their functions?

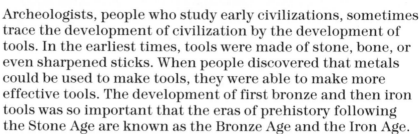

Metals and Early Development of Civilization

A projectile point made of rock, found in Ontario, and believed to date back to 1000 BC to 500 BC

Roman scale armor

Archeologists, people who study early civilizations, sometimes trace the development of civilization by the development of tools. In the earliest times, tools were made of stone, bone, or even sharpened sticks. When people discovered that metals could be used to make tools, they were able to make more effective tools. The development of first bronze and then iron tools was so important that the eras of prehistory following the Stone Age are known as the Bronze Age and the Iron Age.

At first metals that occur in their native, or pure, form were discovered. However, some metals rarely are found. Nuggets of gold, silver, and copper probably caught the attention of pre-historic people because of their shine. Gold and silver were used for ornaments but proved to be too soft for tools. However, copper could be hardened by hammering.

It was only with the discovery of the process of smelting copper ores, however, that metals began to have a significant impact on early societies. When heated, copper becomes a liquid. In the liquid state it can be cast into various shapes. This process must have been unique at the time because it was reversible. Copper implements could be melted down again and cast into new shapes. Even more important, however, was the fact that numerous implements could be made from the same moulds. Casting allowed tools to be mass-produced.

Early attempts at smelting probably involved the use of ores that contained other metals as well as copper. The most important of these impurities proved to be tin, because when it was melted down with copper it produced an alloy, bronze. Bronze is much harder than pure copper and quickly replaced pure copper for most uses.

The Bronze Age

The Bronze Age in the eastern Mediterranean lasted from approximately 4000 BC to 1500 BC. During this time, bronze was used to make everything from axes to needles, armor to swords.

The discovery of bronze also marked the beginning of trade. The production of bronze requires both copper and tin, and deposits of ores containing these two metals seldom occur together. As a result, communities that had been self-sufficient up to this time needed to trade more extensively to obtain sufficient quantities of both metals. This involved developments in navigation, geography, and other arts. It also involved the introduction of coins, which freed traders from relying simply on the trading of goods. These coins were made from silver and gold so that transactions of great value could be made conveniently.

During this period, bronze was used mainly by wealthy people. Copper and tin were still scarce metals and therefore were quite valuable. Bronze implements made little impact on the lives of the common people.

The Iron Age

The Iron Age in the eastern Mediterranean lasted from approximately 1400 BC to AD 50. Iron products were superior to bronze in both strength and durability. However, iron was much more difficult to work with because instead of liquifying when heated, it turned into a spongy mass. This spongy mass had to be heated until it glowed and then it had to be beaten or forged into the desired shape. This process meant that each item had to be made individually. Mass-production casting that was used to make bronze implements could not be used for objects made of iron.

Iron, however, was much more abundant than either copper or tin. As a result iron and its alloy, steel, changed the lives of common people as well as those of wealthy people. Iron axes and saws could be used to cut timber more easily; iron ploughs and hoes improved agriculture. Iron weapons and armor enabled all of the soldiers in an army to be well equipped, not only the nobles.

Historians believe that this fact contributed to the success of the Hittite invasion of the Egyptian empire in the fourteenth century BC. The Hittites were the first people to forge iron weapons in quantity. The Egyptian empire was the last great civilization of the Bronze Age.

Ancient Greek silver coin

Connections

ACTIVITY 7 — Investigating Metallic Properties

In this activity, you will investigate some of the properties of four common substances. Three of these are metallic: iron, copper, and aluminum. The other, chalk, is non-metallic.

Materials

copper wire (or another copper object)
aluminum wire (or another aluminum object)
metal coat hanger (or another object containing iron)
piece of chalk
steel wool
candle
clock or timer
magnet
two 1.5-V batteries
wire leads
flashlight bulb and socket
tray or saucer
paper towel
vinegar
hammer
heavy metal block
safety goggles

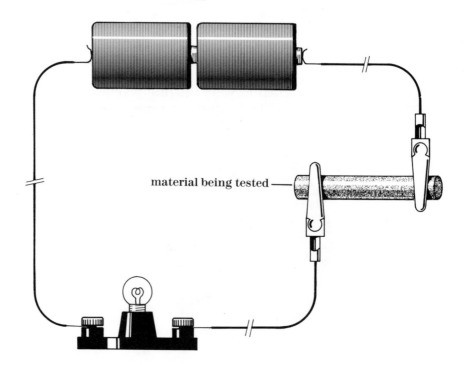

material being tested ——

Procedure

1. Clean the metal objects with steel wool.
2. Examine the first four substances. Note their color and whether they are shiny or dull. Record your observations.
3. Use the magnet to determine which of the four substances are magnetic and which are not. Record your observations.
4. Light the candle. Hold each substance in the candle flame so that the tip of the flame is 10 cm from your finger. Count the seconds until you first feel the substance under your finger getting warm. Record your observations.
5. Connect the batteries, bulb, and a piece of each substance as shown. Clip or touch the free ends of the leads to the ends of the substance to be tested.
6. Place the end of your copper wire on the metal block and hit it sharply with the hammer. *Wear safety goggles when hammering these substances to protect your eyes. Be sure that no one else is too close.* Record your observations.
7. If practical, repeat step 6 for the other three substances.
8. Put a piece of paper towel in a tray or saucer. Moisten the paper towel with vinegar. Place the four substances side by side on top of the moistened towel and leave them overnight. Observe and record any changes in the substances the next day.

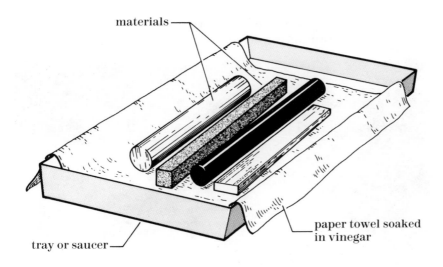

materials

paper towel soaked in vinegar

tray or saucer

Discussion

1. Use your observations to rank the substances as follows.
   a) the most magnetic
   b) the least magnetic
   c) the best conductor of heat
   d) the poorest conductor of heat
   e) the hardest
   f) the softest
   g) the most resistant to corrosion or rust
   h) the least resistant to corrosion or rust
2. What properties are shared by all four substances? Can you think of any metals not used in the experiment which share these properties? Which ones do *not* share these properties?

6.8

Properties of Metals

You can observe eight common properties that are characteristic of most metals. Notice that there are some exceptions.
1. Most metals are solids (although mercury is a liquid).
2. Most metals are silver or grey in color (although copper is reddish brown and gold is yellow).
3. Most metals are shiny; they reflect light.
4. Most metals are good conductors of electricity.
5. Most metals are good conductors of heat.
6. Most metals are **malleable**. In other words, they can be bent without breaking. They can be shaped by hammering.

Modern sports equipment like this tennis racquet is now being made from graphite because of its strength and light weight.

7. Some metals exhibit strong magnetic properties; in particular, iron, nickel, and cobalt.

8. Some metals corrode; iron, in particular, rusts. **Corrosion**
   is an example of a chemical change in which a new substance is created. Oxygen acting upon iron will create a new
   substance, iron oxide, commonly known as rust. Other
   metals such as tin, zinc, gold, and nickel, are far more
   resistant to corrosion.

**The corrosion of copper results in a green copper oxide. The roofs
of Montreal's City Hall are a good example of this.**

Because of these properties, metals can be used for special
purposes. For example, copper is used for electrical wiring
both because it is a good conductor of electricity and because
it is malleable. It is a better conductor of electricity than
either aluminum or iron, although it is a poorer conductor
than either silver or gold. The malleability of copper is also
important for its use in electrical wiring. If copper were brittle, it would break every time someone bent an electric power
cord.

Now consider stainless steel. It is often used for cooking
utensils because it is a good conductor of heat and it does not
react chemically with foods. While some pots may be made
entirely of stainless steel, it is more usual for the handle to be
made from some other material that is a good thermal insulator. With a handle made from wood or plastic, the pot can be
picked up without using a pot holder. At the same time, pots
with such handles cannot be used in an oven because wood or
plastic will burn. Pots made entirely from stainless steel can
be used either in the oven or on the top of a stove.

Canoes sometimes are made of aluminum because it is durable and light.

Questions

1. What properties of metals make them different from other materials?
2. Why are metals used almost exclusively for electrical wiring?
3. Which metals seem to corrode the most easily?

Summary

Substances with similar appearances often have different chemical properties. A knowledge of chemical properties and chemical reactions can help you to distinguish substances from one another. This knowledge can also help you to be a careful consumer.

You can classify substances as acids, bases, or neutral substances. Acidic substances have different properties from basic ones. Acids and bases can neutralize each other.

Metals are a special group of substances which share common properties. Among these properties are conductivity of heat and electricity, magnetism and malleability. These properties make metals very useful in our world.

Lava samples are collected to determine the composition.

Chapter Questions

Remember

1. Name three substances that
   a) dissolve in water
   b) do not dissolve in water.
2. How are crystalline substances different from non-crystalline substances?
3. a) Name five properties of acids.
   b) Name five properties of bases.
4. Name four properties that all metals seem to share.
5. What does it mean to say that a metal is malleable? Name three materials that are *not* malleable.
6. a) Give one example illustrating how acid rain is formed.
   b) Name three ways in which acid rain is harmful to our environment.

Think

1. a) You are given a white powder that fizzes when vinegar is added to it, but turns blue when iodine solution is added. What do you think it might be? Why?
   b) You are given a white powder that dissolves in water. It starts to liquify and then turns brown when heated. Yet it seems to consist of two different kinds of crystals. What might it be? Why?

2. Why is it unwise to store acids in metal containers?

3. Sour milk is sometimes used in baking pancakes and biscuits to make them light. It reacts to produce bubbles of carbon dioxide gas which expand as the pancakes or biscuits are heated. What kind of substance in the sour milk helps to create this chemical reaction?

4. Swimming pools are usually tested every day to determine the pH of the water. Try to answer these questions about swimming pools.

   a) What pH level is considered desirable?

   b) What is used to lower the pH? raise it?

For sanitary reasons it is important to control the pH of swimming pools.

5. Shampoos are often advertised as *pH balanced*. What does this mean?

6. In tests of the electrical conductivity of different materials, it might be difficult to get samples of the same thickness, shape, and length. How would these factors affect the conductivity? What would you have to do in order to have a fair test of the electrical conductivity?

7. In spite of its high cost, gold is used instead of copper to make some electrical connections in microcomputers. Why?

8. Specify as many uses as you can for aluminum foil. Which properties of aluminum suit it for each use?

9. Tin cans are made primarily of steel with a thin coating of tin on the outside. What is the purpose of this coating of tin?

Dream

1. Steel is probably the most commonly used metal today. Suppose you were to discover a new material to replace steel. What ideal properties would this metal have?

Some parts of car engines are made from ceramic materials to reduce both the weight and friction.

Decide

1. Salt is used on many Canadian roads in winter to remove ice and snow. What harmful effect does this salt have on cars. Is this harm balanced by the improved safety of our roads?

2. Recently, plastics and other substances have been substituted for steel and other metals in construction of automobiles. Suggest some of the advantages and disadvantages of this substitution.

7

Using Energy

A race car uses hundreds of litres of fuel in an hour. During a race, it will make several pit stops to fill its fuel tank. A race car needs fuel. A driver needs food. At a pit stop, the car will be filled with fuel, the driver may drink a glass of orange juice.

Racing fuel and orange juice are both sources of **energy**, but each can work only for a suitable energy user. Orange juice provides the driver with energy, but it is useless to the race car. Similarly, the driver's body cannot use racing fuel.

There are many ways of using energy besides burning fuel or eating food. Here are five animals and five machines, each of which is suited to use energy in a certain way. You have already seen how your body has something in common with a race car. See if you can match each animal with the machine that uses energy in a similar way.

a) Sunning lizard

b) Camera

c) Human eye

d) Helicopter blades

e) Fennec fox's ears

f) Car radiator fan

g) Dragonfly's wings

h) Solar home

i) Elephant's flapping ear

j) Satellite dish

You have just seen some ways in which energy is used. Energy makes things happen. Energy is difficult to define, but you can learn to identify some of its forms and learn how it is used. By learning about energy, you can use it wisely.

7.1

Forms of Energy

A rainbow shows the many colors of visible radiant energy.

The small antennas on this microwave tower send and receive signals.

In the introduction to this chapter, you looked at some of the many forms of energy. Each form of energy can be classified as either **radiant energy** or **non-radiant energy**.

Radiant Energy

All forms of energy that behave like light are called radiant energy. They are also referred to as **radiation**. Radiant energy travels at the speed of light, 300 000 km/s.

Our eyes are sensitive to visible light, which is one form of radiant energy. Visible light makes sight possible. Our eyes see many colors of light, like those in this rainbow.

All other forms of radiant energy cannot be seen. Here are some examples of invisible radiant energy.

Radiowaves are used to send radio and television signals from a television station to the receiver in your home.

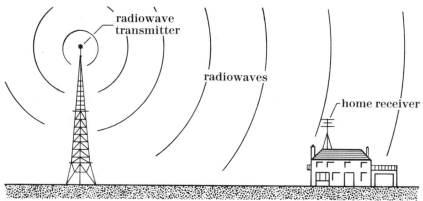

Microwaves might be familiar to you as the source of heat in a microwave oven. Microwaves are also used to send television and telephone signals across the country and to satellites.

Infra-red radiation can be felt. Like microwaves, this form of radiant energy produces heat. Infra-red radiation from the sun warms you. Fast-food counters use it to keep food warm.

Ultraviolet radiation produces sunburn or tans skin.

X rays can be harmful in large amounts. Doctors use X rays in small doses to see inside the body.

Gamma rays are similar to X rays, and can also be very dangerous. But in hospitals, special machines can produce controlled gamma rays for cancer treatment.

Sunbathers are warmed by the sun's infra-red radiation. They cannot feel the ultraviolet radiation but it does affect their skin.

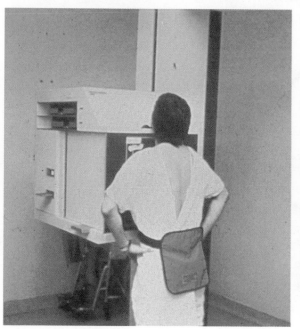

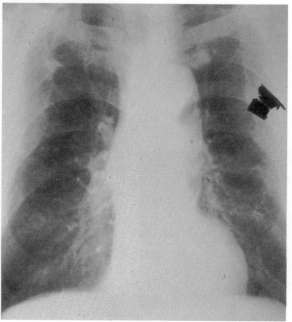

X rays produced by machines can pass through the body to produce a photograph.

Non-radiant Energy

Non-radiant energy is the energy possessed by objects. There are two kinds of non-radiant energy: **kinetic energy** and **potential energy**.

Kinetic Energy

The energy of moving objects is called kinetic energy. A moving ball has kinetic energy. A ball at rest does not have kinetic energy. A car moving along the street has kinetic energy. So does a food processor when its blades are moving.

Heat is a form of kinetic energy. Heat turns water into steam.

Sound is another form of kinetic energy. When you speak, you make the air move. A stereo speaker also makes the air move. Your ears respond to these movements of the air.

Electricity is a third form of kinetic energy. Electricity is used to run many machines.

Huge sound speakers are needed at rock concerts.

Steam locomotives use heat energy to move.

Lightning bolts are an impressive display of electricity.

Hugh Le Caine: Pioneer of Electronic Music

Hugh Le Caine was born in Port Arthur (Thunder Bay), Ontario, in 1914. His father was an inventor and an electrician who worked as an engineer at local grain elevators. As a boy, Le Caine enjoyed music and experimented with new musical instruments. He built an electronic ukulele while still in high school.

After he completed high school, Le Caine studied piano for a year in Toronto. He then entered the engineering and physics program at Queen's University in Kingston, Ontario. While there, he learned how to describe sound in a scientific way.

Le Caine worked during the summers in the nuclear research laboratory at Queen's. In the summer of 1937, he developed his first successful electronic musical instrument. This was a pipe organ in which the reeds were operated by electricity, giving the player more control over the music. Le Caine discovered that this electrical system was also useful in the nuclear research laboratory.

After graduating in 1939, Le Caine went to Ottawa to do research on radar and microwave transmission with the National Research Council (NRC). On his own, he continued to invent electronic musical instruments, such as an electronic keyboard which he called the *Sackbut*. He worked on it between 1946 and 1948. Like modern keyboards, the *Sackbut* produced a wide variety of sounds.

Hugh Le Caine with his electronic keyboard, the Sackbut

By 1955, he had invented an electronic organ. A piano company even bought the design for it. Le Caine's success convinced the NRC to set up a laboratory to design new electronic musical instruments.

Electronic music was just starting in the 1950s. Few new instruments like Le Caine's were available. In 1959, Le Caine was asked to help open a studio designed for electronic music at the University of Toronto. This studio gave musicians a chance to experiment with electronic music.

Later, Le Caine worked on systems similar to those now used in modern synthesizers. Hugh Le Caine died in 1977, but his work in both science and music are well remembered.

Another electronic musical instrument invented by Hugh Le Caine was the touch-sensitive organ.

Potential Energy

Energy stored inside a material or an object is called potential energy.

Elastic potential energy is stored in anything that is stretched, compressed, or twisted out of shape that will snap back to its original form. Elastic bands have this kind of potential energy. So does a golf ball.

Gravitational potential energy is stored in anything that is above the ground. The water in a waterfall has gravitational potential energy at the top of the cliff.

Chemical potential energy is stored in fuels such as wood, oil, or gas. These fuels release energy when they are burned. Chemical potential energy is stored in food. Food releases energy in your body and enables you to live.

This oil rig is not on fire. Natural gas from the drill hole is being burned off. The light and heat are produced from the chemical potential energy of the fuel.

The dark streaks in this rock are evidence of uranium.

Nuclear potential energy is stored in special fuels like uranium that produce heat inside a nuclear reactor.

A classification system for all forms of energy might look like this.

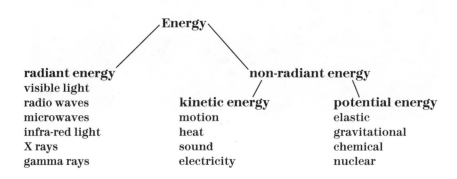

Questions

1. How many forms of radiant energy do you use around your home? Name them and describe where they are used.

2. Which form of potential energy makes each of the following happen?
   a) A firecracker explodes.
   b) A rain drop falls.
   c) A rocket launches.
   d) An atomic bomb explodes.

3. Which form of energy described in this section is most important to you? Explain your choice.

Energy is changing from one form to another all around you. Look at this illustration. What energy changes are taking place?

7.2

Energy Conversions and Converters

When you walk, the chemical energy stored in your body is changed into kinetic energy. Some of the kinetic energy is in the motion of walking. The rest of the kinetic energy is in the form of heat. You can describe this change using this statement.

chemical energy ⟶ kinetic energy + heat
                   (motion of walking)

When you put a battery in a radio and turn on the radio, the chemical energy stored in the battery is changed into sound and heat.

chemical energy ⟶ sound energy + heat

Energy changes like these are called **energy conversions**. Your body and the radio are acting as **energy converters**. All energy conversions produce heat. In fact, any conversion will usually produce more than one form of energy. Any energy conversion can be written in the form of a statement.

energy
converter

energy form used $\longrightarrow$ energy form produced

For example, a flashlight uses **chemical energy** to produce visible light and heat. You can write an energy conversion statement for a flashlight.

flashlight

chemical energy $\longrightarrow$ visible light + heat

ACTIVITY 1   Describing Forms of Energy Conversions

In this activity, you will identify the energy forms both used and produced by toys or small appliances.

Materials

variety of different toys or small appliances

Procedure

1. Label the toy or appliance with your name so that it can be identified by your classmates.
2. Place all of the toys and small appliances in one location.
3. Select a toy or appliance and examine it.
4. Record the name of the toy or appliance.
5. Identify and record the form of energy used to make it work and the form of energy it produces.
6. Repeat steps 3, 4, and 5 for several different toys or appliances.

Discussion

1. From your observations, classify the toys or appliances according to the form of energy used and the form of energy produced.
2. Compare the observations for your toy or appliance with the observations of your classmates. Discuss any differences with them.
3. List any forms of energy which you did not see during this activity. Be as specific as possible. Suggest some other toy or appliance which would use or produce these forms of energy.

Extension

1. Design a machine which uses elastic potential energy to produce kinetic energy in order to carry an egg across the floor. Have a contest to see which design can carry the egg **a)** the farthest and **b)** the fastest, without breaking it.

Natural Energy Converters

The sun is a natural energy converter. Like all stars, it changes **nuclear energy** into different forms of radiant energy. Some of this energy strikes our planet, where it is converted in different ways.

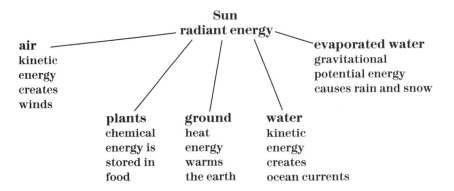

Sun
radiant energy

air
kinetic
energy
creates
winds

plants
chemical
energy is
stored in
food

ground
heat
energy
warms
the earth

water
kinetic
energy
creates
ocean currents

evaporated water
gravitational
potential energy
causes rain and snow

Animals are also natural energy converters. Energy conversions occur in all parts of an animal's body, such as the muscles, eyes, and ears.

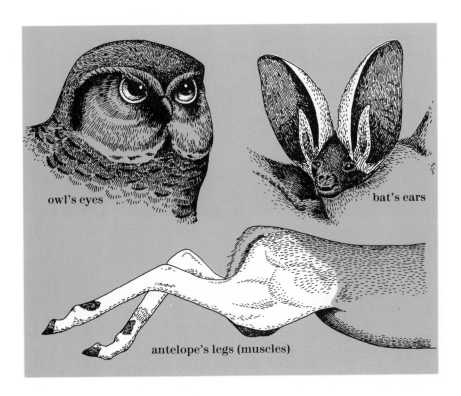

owl's eyes

bat's ears

antelope's legs (muscles)

Questions

1. Write each of the statements below in this form.

energy
converter
energy form used $\longrightarrow$ energy form produced

a) The sun turns nuclear energy into radiant energy.
b) Lightning is produced from the kinetic energy of ice particles and rain drops in clouds.
c) To produce light and heat, a firefly uses the chemical energy in the food it consumes.

Inventions to Convert Energy

All living creatures naturally carry out a variety of energy conversions in order to survive. Humans have also invented machines to increase their use and production of energy.

You can buy heating devices that use electricity or chemical fuels such as oil, natural gas, or electricity. Food production equipment ranges from farm machines and food packagers to kitchen refrigerators and kettles. Imagine the chemical energy that is converted by the engines of a jumbo jet as it climbs several kilometres into the sky. Energy converters such as lasers and radiation therapy machines, which change electricity into radiant energy, help doctors treat cancer and other diseases.

Radio, television, and communications satellites have made worldwide broadcasts possible. These devices change electricity to various other forms of energy. Computerized telephone systems can let you call almost anywhere in seconds. All these things are manufactured by people using a wide variety of energy-converting devices. Manufactured energy converters are found almost everywhere you look. They are an important part of your life. You should be aware of how they are used in your community.

Light flows through optical fibres in much the same way that water flows through pipes. The thin optical fibres (held in the hand above) can be used instead of electrical wires to send telephone signals.

Questions

1. Write the statement for the energy conversion accomplished by each of the following familiar inventions.

   a) a stereo speaker
   b) a telephone mouthpiece
   c) a dishwasher
   d) an elevator
   e) a gasoline lawnmower
   f) a laser

2. What do you think is the most important energy converter invented in each of these categories? Be prepared to defend your opinion. There is no one *correct* answer.
   a) transportation
   b) communication
   c) food production
3. Electrical energy can be converted into most other forms of energy. List four possible conversions and name an invention which can carry out each conversion.

Investigating Energy Conversions in the Community

In this activity, you will investigate some energy conversions in your community.

Materials

energy-converting devices in your community

(If necessary, get help from your parents or an adult responsible for the equipment involved. *Do not handle any equipment with which you are unfamiliar.*)

Procedure

1. Identify some energy-converting devices that you can find in your community. Here is a list of places you can look.
   a) the home
   b) the school
   c) the arena
   d) the farm
   e) the car

Home

Arena

Farm

2. For each device you have identified in question 1, describe the energy conversion. What forms of energy are wasted by each device? Make a table like the one below and record your observations.

Energy- Converting Devices	Energy Conversion	Energy Produced	
		Useful Energy	Wasted Energy

Discussion

1. How many of the energy-converting devices that you found would be classified as **a)** essential or **b)** non-essential? Why?
2. What were the most common forms of **a)** energy used and **b)** energy produced?
3. Could any of the devices that you found be replaced by other kinds of energy-converting devices? If so, describe what they are.

Extension

1. From your table of observations, design an advertisement for one of the energy-converting devices. The advertisement should include all of the information on the conversion device found in your table.

7.3

Sources of Energy

No energy conversion can take place without a source of energy. The earth's surface receives its energy from three major natural sources: the sun, the moon, and the earth's interior.

The sun is the most important source of energy for the earth. The radiant energy of the sun is **solar energy**. This energy is produced from nuclear energy released deep inside its surface. As it approaches the earth, most of this solar energy is reflected by clouds in the atmosphere. The energy that does reach the earth's surface is absorbed by dry ground, water, air, and green plants.

The moon, with some help from the sun, pulls on the oceans, creating the tides. These tides provide a source of gravitational energy.

Geothermal energy is produced inside the earth by several kinds of energy conversions. This heat reaches the surface of

the earth in the form of volcanoes, hot springs, and geysers.
    This figure illustrates the flow of energy to the earth's sur-
face. All of these energy sources are **renewable energy
sources**. In other words, they will last as long as the earth
itself lasts.

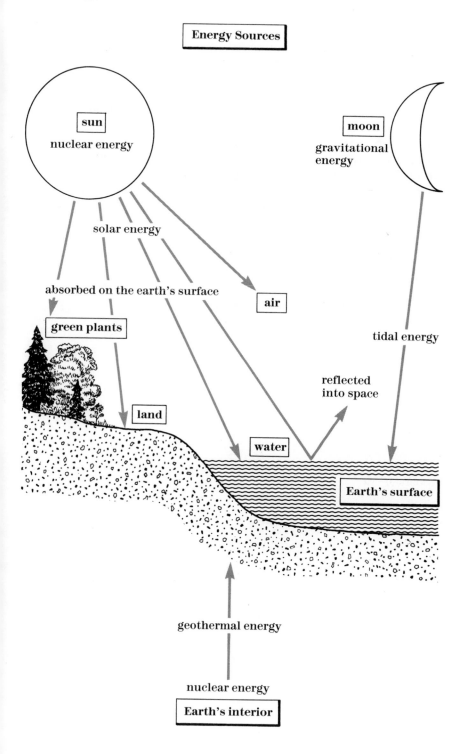

Energy can be stored in a concentrated form in substances called **fuels**. Most fuels used today are **fossil fuels**. These fossil fuels contain chemical energy produced from the sun's radiant energy by prehistoric plants. Coal is an example of a fossil fuel.

Uranium found in rocks contains nuclear potential energy. It is used to produce electricity.

Fossil fuels and uranium are examples of **non-renewable energy sources**. Even if the supply of these fuels seems unlimited, it is not. Eventually the supply will be used up. There is no way to replace it.

Plants are continuously producing fuel. For example, wood and peat also contain chemical energy produced from sunlight. Energy produced from living or recently dead plants and animals is called **biomass energy**. Biomass is limited but it can be replaced. It is a renewable energy source.

This figure illustrates an overview of the history of energy use.

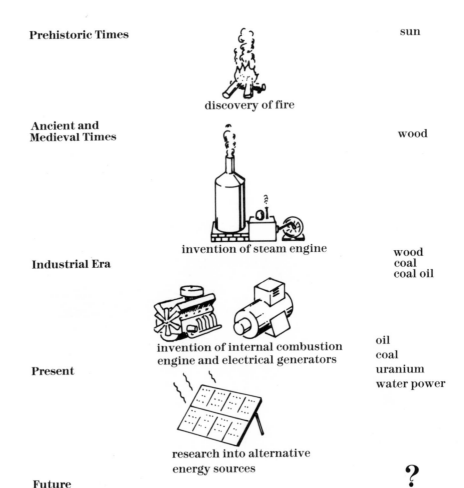

Prehistoric Times

discovery of fire

sun

Ancient and Medieval Times

invention of steam engine

wood

Industrial Era

wood
coal
coal oil

invention of internal combustion engine and electrical generators

oil
coal

Present

uranium
water power

research into alternative energy sources

Future

?

Questions

1. Name the three major sources of energy for the earth's surface.
2. Which source provides most of the energy received on the earth's surface?
3. How does the moon supply energy to the earth's surface?
4. Describe geothermal energy.
5. What is a fuel?
6. Explain the difference between a renewable and a non-renewable energy source.

Unlike many animals, humans have no thick layers of fat and fur to protect them from the cold. Even so, we can keep warm by using the materials and energy in our environment.

7.4

Using Energy Wisely

Insulation

Heat always flows from the substance with the higher temperature to the one with the lower temperature. Insulators can be used to slow down the flow of heat. Clothing is an insulator. It controls heat flow to and from the body by trapping air near the body where it is warmed. Homes are insulated to keep in heat during the winter and keep out heat during the summer.

If you know how well different materials insulate, you can make good energy-saving decisions in the future. Which materials works best to slow down the flow of heat energy?

These divers are kept warm by the water trapped inside their wetsuits.

Comparing Insulation Materials

In this activity, you will co-operate with your classmates to compare several insulation materials.

Materials

2 tin cans, one larger than the other
thermometer
timer (a watch or the classroom clock)

Natural Insulators	Artificial Insulators
furs	styrofoam
feathers	fibreglass
cotton	rayon
wool	
wood chips	
paper	

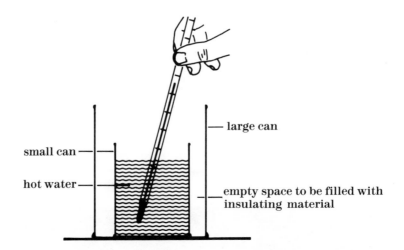

large can

small can

hot water

empty space to be filled with insulating material

Procedure

1. Make a table like the one below

Insulating Material	Initial Temperature	Time for a Temperature Drop of 10°C

2. Place the empty, smaller can inside the larger one as shown. Leave at least 1 cm of space between the walls of the two cans.

3. Fill the smaller can with hot water (about 80°C to 90°C). For convenience, heat the water in a kettle.

4. Hold the thermometer in the water. Make sure that it does not touch the sides or bottom of the can. As soon as the thermometer gives a steady reading, record this initial temperature and start your timer.

5. In your table, record the time it takes for the temperature of the water to drop 10°C.

6. Empty the water from the smaller can. Put the smaller can back into the larger can. Fill the space between the cans with one of the insulating materials.

7. Repeat steps 3 through 6 for each of the insulating materials. Be sure that the initial temperature is the same one you recorded in step 4.

Discussion

1. Which material allowed the water to cool the fastest? Is this material the best insulator or the worst one?

2. Rank the materials from the best insulator down to the worst one. Which was the best natural insulator? Which was the best artificial one?

3. Even though some materials rank lower on your list, they might be preferred as insulators. Can you suggest why?

4. What effect does tight packing have on the insulating property of a material?

People have always found some way to insulate their homes. This prairie sod house, photographed in 1900, is an example.

Extension

1. Obtain some insulation materials at a builders' supply store. Compare them to the materials used in your experiment.
2. Repeat the experiment and measure the temperature at 30-s intervals until the temperature drops by 10°C. Plot a graph of temperature versus time for each material and compare them. Explain the shape of each graph.

Heat and Cooling

In cold weather, buildings need **heating systems** to replace heat that is lost through walls, roofs, windows, and doors.

A heating system converts one of various forms of energy to heat energy. The heat spreads through a building by the flow of hot air through ducts, or by the flow of hot water through pipes. A heating system is controlled by a **thermostat** that is set at a certain temperature. The thermostat then can turn the heating system on and off so that the temperature inside the building stays close to the set temperature.

To decrease the amount of energy a heating system uses to heat a building, the amount of heat lost to the outside can be decreased by using insulation and by stopping air leaks. The thermostat can also be set at a lower temperature.

In hot weather, air conditioners cool warm air that enters buildings from the outside. The amount of energy an air conditioner uses to cool air can also be decreased by using insulation and by stopping air leaks.

Which house has more insulation under its roof?

Monitoring Variations in Building Temperature

Is the temperature inside a building the same everywhere? In this activity, you will investigate how well the temperature is controlled inside your home or school.

Materials

thermometer
metre stick

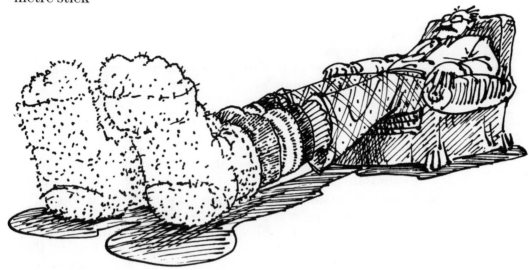

Procedure

1. Select one room to investigate thoroughly. In the case of your school, the class can divide the work. Draw an outline of the floor area in the room and label the inner walls, outer walls, windows, doors, and heat vents.

2. Record the temperature 5 cm from each wall at a spot 1 m above the floor. Try to choose locations away from a door, window, or heat vent. Be sure to let the thermometer reach a stable temperature at each spot. Wait 1 min before reading the temperature for all measurements.

3. Record the temperature 5 cm from the centre of all closed windows and doors and from the opening of the heat vent.

4. Record the temperature in the middle of the room 1 m above the floor. Also record the temperature as near to the ceiling as you can above this spot.

5. For the whole building, pick selected spots to record temperatures. Include several measurements on each floor and special rooms like the furnace room. Measure at the same spot in each location, for example, the middle of the area and 1 m above the floor. Note any features of the location that would affect the temperature.

Discussion

1. What is the coolest location in the room? Why is it the coolest?
2. What is the warmest location in the room? Why is it the warmest?
3. How do the temperatures at the two heights in the middle of the room compare? See step 4. Suggest a reason for any difference.
4. Which floor is warmest? Which floor is coldest? Suggest a reason for your answers.
5. How does the temperature in the furnace room compare with the measurements in the rest of the building? Why?
6. Based on your results, can you suggest any ways to make the temperature more even throughout the building?

Extension

1. Compare the temperature of the air from various vents in the building. Suggest a reason for differences that you find.
2. Locate an outside wall which has no windows or doors. Measure the temperature along the inside of the wall at 0.5-m intervals at floor level. Repeat the measurements at heights of 0.5 m, 1.0 m, and 1.5 m. Continue increasing the height until you reach the ceiling. Draw a map of the wall, labelling the temperature at each location. Connect areas of equal temperature with a line. These lines are called **isotherms.** How can isotherms be used to locate areas where insulation has deteriorated?
3. Obtain an infra-red photograph of a house or a building. If possible, take an infra-red photograph of your house or school. Analyse the photographs to discover where heat is escaping.

This is an infra-red photograph (called a thermogram) of a house. The lighter blue colors show where most of the heat loss occurs. The window to the left of the door is single-glazed and therefore lets more heat escape than do the other windows, which are double-glazed.

Electrical Energy Use

Electricity is one of the most convenient forms of energy in your daily life. It might seem to be in endless supply, but this is not necessarily so. Electricity must be produced from some other form of energy. At a waterfall, for example, the potential energy of falling water is used to create electricity.

The chemical energy of coal can also produce electricity, but the amount of coal in the world is limited. Fuels such as natural gas, oil, and uranium are limited too. Besides, creating electricity from these sources can result in air pollutants and other dangerous wastes. You can see how important it is to conserve electricity.

Energy is usually measured in units called **joules**. The symbol for a joule is **J**. Each appliance in your home uses energy at a different rate. The kitchen stove uses energy much more rapidly than a plug-in radio does. Every appliance has a label indicating the rate at which it uses electricity. This is called the **power rating**.

Like electrical appliances, runners use energy. Some use it more rapidly than others, so you could say that they have a higher power rating.

The rate at which a device uses electricity is measured in joules per second or **watts**. The symbol for a watt is **W**.

$$\text{power (W)} = \frac{\text{energy used (J)}}{\text{time (s)}}$$

For example, a light bulb rated at 60 W uses 60 J of electrical energy every second. The energy used by the bulb is calculated as 60 J multiplied by the number of seconds it is lit.

$$\text{energy used (J)} = \text{power (W)} \times \text{time (s)}$$

In 60 seconds, the energy used is calculated as follows.

$$\text{energy used} = 60 \text{ W} \times 60 \text{ s}$$
$$= 3600 \text{ J}$$

ACTIVITY 5 Estimating Energy Use of Appliances

In this activity, you can discover the power ratings for your appliances. You will use them to estimate the amount of energy used.

Materials

appliances (or owner's manuals)

Procedure

1. Make a table like the one below.

Appliance	Power Rating (W)	Time Used Each Day (s)	Time Used Each Year (s)	Estimated Yearly Energy Use (J)
hair dryer	1000	120	120 × 365 = 43 800	43 800 000

2. Find and record in a table the power ratings for at least five appliances used in your home. Find the power rating on the appliance.
3. Estimate in seconds the time that this appliance is used each day and record your estimate in the table (for example, 2 min = 120 s).
4. Calculate the number of seconds each appliance would operate in one year. To do this, multiply your figure from step 3 by 365.

5. Calculate the energy you would estimate that each appliance would use in a year. Use this equation.

energy used (J) = power (W) × time (s)

6. Convert the estimate to megajoules (MJ).
1 MJ = 1 000 000 J. The hair dryer in the table would use 43.8 MJ in one year.

Discussion

1. Which appliances use the most electrical energy? Which appliances use the least?
2. Compare your results with those of other students in your class. Revise your estimates and extend your table to include appliances that were not part of your study.

ACTIVITY 6

Reading an Electrical Meter

Electrical energy is also measured in units of **kilowatt hours (kW·h)**. A kilowatt hour represents the amount of energy in one kilowatt (1000 W) acting for one hour. One kilowatt hour would therefore be equal to 3.6 MJ.

Meters attached to a house or a building record the number of kilowatt hours used. If you know how to read these meters, you can measure the daily consumption of electricity in your home or other buildings. Meters are generally found either in the basement or on the outside wall of a building. The dials will take one of two forms.

four-dial meter 1348 kW·h

five-dial meter 35 721 kW·h

Materials

electrical meter

Procedure

1. Record the reading on the meter at the same time of day for seven consecutive mornings.
2. If you live in a house, keep a record of the use of major electrical appliances for each day. Note if your house uses an electrical furnace, an air conditioner, or a heat pump.

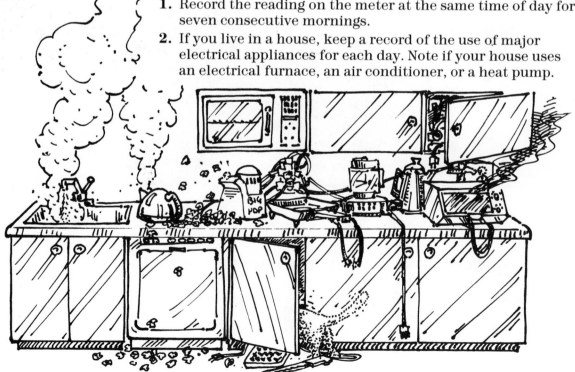

Discussion

1. On which days was the use of electricity greatest? On which days was it the least?
2. How many kilowatt hours are used during the week?
3. Compare your use of electricity during the week with that of other students in your class. Whose home used the most? the least? Suggest a reason for these differences.
4. Find the cost per kilowatt hour of electricity. Calculate the cost of the electricity used for the week.
5. How much electricity is used in a year? Estimate this amount of electricity or find out from utility bills.

Extension

1. Find the gas meter in your home or school. What units are used for measuring gas? Record the meter reading each day at the same time for a week. Answer discussion questions 1 and 3 for the use of gas.
2. Locate where the major sources of energy (electricity, gas, oil) enter your school, where the energy is converted (furnace, air conditioner), and how the energy is transported through the school. Make a list of the forms of energy used. Match each form with the source.
3. Compare the use of energy to heat your home or school at different times of the year or during periods when the temperatures are different. How does the outside temperature affect the amount of energy used for heating?
4. What appears to be the major energy consumer in your school or home? Gather data to support your opinion.

In the past, wood was a major fuel. Here, two schoolteachers prepare for class.

ACTIVITY 7

Planning Ways to Save Energy

In our homes and schools, a lot of energy is wasted. There are three ways in which energy can be saved: reduction, recycling, and renovation.

You are practising energy reduction if you close the refrigerator door quickly after getting what you want. If you use heat from the clothes dryer to keep the laundry room warm, you are recycling energy. Adding insulation in the walls and attics of a building is a means of saving energy through renovation.

In this activity, you will develop a plan to save energy in your school or home.

Materials

reference materials on energy conservation

Procedure

1. Work as part of a group to develop the plan.
2. List some specific ways to save energy in your home or school. Use the three categories (reduction, recycling, and renovation), adding three examples to each category.

3. Estimate the money saved in one year for as many of your group's examples as possible. To make this estimate, use the steps listed in Activities 5 and 6.

4. Compare your ideas and estimates with those of other groups. Revise them if you discover new information.

5. Form your group's plan to save energy. Divide the plan into three sections.
   a) reduction
   b) recycling
   c) renovation

Discussion

1. Are there alternative energy sources that you might use in your plan?

2. What problems might these sources create?

Extension

1. How would you test the results of your energy-saving plan?

2. Find out how your school and school board are attempting to cut down on the costs of electricity and heating.

3. Visit building sites in the community and observe new construction methods designed to save energy.

4. Look at television, newspapers, and magazines for commercials and advertisements related to energy saving. Using what you have watched and read, make a collection of ideas. List these ideas in the three categories: reduction, recycling, and renovation.

Questions

1. In which direction does heat flow?
   a) from a cooler to a warmer substance
   b) from a warmer to a cooler substance

2. How is home insulation like clothing?

3. What does a thermostat do?

4. Where else besides the walls and roof should you find insulation in your home?

5. Why is it difficult to make all areas of a house equal in temperature?

The Science of Music

Most musical instruments create sounds by using the vibrations of strings, surfaces, or columns of air. The instruments convert the kinetic energy of the moving air into sound energy.

In stringed instruments, the length and thickness of a vibrating string determine the pitch of the note produced. Shorter, thinner strings produce higher-pitched notes. Tightening or loosening the string allows the player to adjust the pitch. Some stringed instruments are the harp, the piano, the guitar, and the violin.

Acoustic guitar

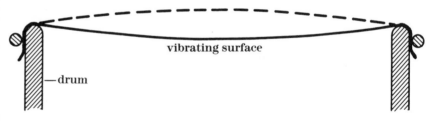

fixed end

vibrating string

length and tightness of string can be adjusted here

In percussion instruments, the size, shape, thickness, and material of a vibrating surface determine the sound produced. In a drum, the tension in the surface of the top also affects the sound. Other percussion instruments are the cymbal, the xylophone, and the bell.

Drums and cymbals

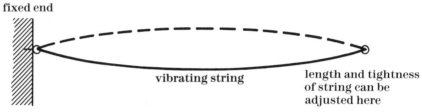

vibrating surface

—drum

In some instruments, a sound is produced by a vibrating column of air. The length of the air column and the shape of the instruments cause the air within the instrument to vibrate in different ways. A shorter air column produces a higher sound. The musician can sometimes change the length of the air col-

Trombone

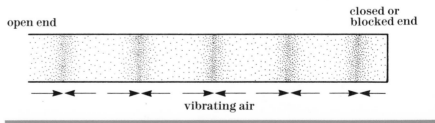

open end

closed or blocked end

vibrating air

umn by using keys or valves. Wind instruments are of two types: woodwind and brass. The flute and the saxophone are examples of the first type; the trombone and trumpet are examples of the second.

In electronic instruments, electricity increases the sound vibrations, making the sound even louder.

Electronic keyboards and synthesizers also use electricity both to produce and to amplify sounds. Electronic instruments can imitate the sounds of other instruments.

Rock groups use electronic instruments such as electric guitars and keyboards.

1. Into which group of instruments would you place each of these instruments?
   a) ukulele
   b) tambourine
   c) pipe organ
2. When drumsticks hit the skin of a drum, what produces the resulting loud sound?
3. Research these questions.
   a) Which instrument of the traditional orchestra makes the widest range of sounds? Why?
   b) Other than percussion instruments, which instrument in the traditional orchestra makes the smallest range of sounds? Why?
4. How does fingering a violin or guitar string change the sound?

Connections

Summary

Energy appears in many different forms. Energy makes things happen when it changes from one form to another.

All living creatures convert energy.

Inventions convert energy and allow people to control their environment. Inventions are used in heating, food production, manufacturing, transportation, communication, and medicine.

Technology extends the use of energy. It can be used to create artificial environments. Heat is controlled in homes and buildings through insulation and heating systems. Homes contain many energy converters, especially those run by electricity.

Canada uses a large amount of energy. Many common energy sources are limited. Awareness of how much energy you use can help you conserve it. New technologies are being developed to use energy more efficiently and to harness alternative sources of energy.

Unlike the familiar farm windmill, the Éole windmill can be driven by winds coming from any direction because of its aircraft-wing shaped blades. The blades are 37 m high and 24 m wide. A joint project of the National Research Council and Hydro-Québec, this windmill is located in the Magdalen Islands in the Gulf of St. Lawrence.

Chapter Questions

Remember

1. Which of these statements are true? Which are false? Rewrite the false statements to make them true.
   a) Energy makes things happen when it changes form.
   b) Gasoline is a form of energy.
   c) An energy converter creates energy.
   d) Heat is always produced in an energy conversion.
   e) Heat insulators produce heat.
   f) Thermostats turn heating systems on and off.
   g) All energy waste could be prevented if energy converters were turned off when not in use.
   h) All energy converters are made by humans.

2. Classify each of the following as kinetic, potential, or radiant energy.
   a) X rays   d) electricity
   b) sound   e) radiowaves
   c) nuclear energy f) gravitational energy

3. For what three major activities do animals use energy?

4. Name two natural and two invented heat insulators.

Think

1. Match one item from list A with the corresponding item from list B.

A	B
a) heating	a) television set
b) food processing	b) train
c) communication	c) threshing machine
d) transportation	d) x-ray machine
e) manufacturing	e) infra-red lamp
f) medicine	f) drill press

2. Write the energy conversion accomplished by the following.
   a) dry-cell battery   c) photographic film
   b) muscle   d) solar cell

3. Name an energy converter which changes the following.
   a) electricity to heat
   b) sound to electricity
   c) electricity to gravitational energy

4. What feature of a car radiator is similar to a feature of an elephant's ear?

5. Suggest four ways to reduce energy waste in these situations.

   a) in the home   **c)** on a farm
   b) throughout a city   **d)** on a ship at sea

What is the energy converter in this transportation system?

Dream

1. Do a research project to find out how animals control energy in their environment.

2. Write an essay or a short story on how energy might be used one hundred years from now.

3. Describe three different energy conversions in your body. Where does each one occur?

Decide

1. Suggest some sources of energy that are not used much now but will be used more in the future. Design a poster to illustrate one of these alternate energy sources. Describe how it will be used in order to produce electricity in large amounts. What would be some of the difficulties involved?

2. Houses are insulated and renovated to reduce the loss of heat and waste energy. Research ways in which this is done by visiting a contractor or building materials store. Which ways do you think are the most effective?

Hot water from deep within the earth can be used to generate electricity. This geothermal energy produces steam at a generating station in New Zealand.

8

Plants in Your Life

Dotted across the open spaces covering much of northern Canada are occasional patches of colorful vegetation. If you look closely at these patches of vegetation, you may notice that they are found around skeletons of animals like muskox and caribou. Why do these plants grow here?

Jawbone of a caribou with tundra flora

Plants grow in a wide variety of environments. Much of northern Canada is covered by expanses of land called tundra. Plants growing on the tundra are usually low-growing shrubs, grasses, and herbs. These plants can survive cold temperatures, weak sunlight, and little precipitation. They also must tolerate the soil conditions of the tundra, which is permanently frozen below a depth of approximately one metre and is usually poor in nutrients.

The plants that grow around the skeletons of large animals also can survive cold temperatures, weak sunlight, and little precipitation. However, these plants need more nutrients from the soil than most plants that grow on the tundra. These nutrients are provided by substances released into the soil by the bodies of the dead animals.

You can see that plants need a variety of conditions to survive. Any plant's survival depends on its ability to cope with its environment. The conditions of water, light, soil, and temperature are all part of this environment.

How are plants suited to some environments, but not to others? Why is it important for us to have plants as part of our environment? This chapter will help you answer these questions.

Tundra landscape, Ellesmere Island

One vital function of a plant is to produce a new generation of plants. In order to do this, some plants produce seeds. What is a seed and how does it work?

Investigation of a Seed

Getting Started: Seed Germination

Burst seed pod of a milkweed plant, exposing the seeds to the wind

This figure shows some bean seeds before and after sprouting. Sprouting is also called **germination**. In order to grow into a plant, a seed must first **germinate**. For germination to occur, what conditions must be present? How important to germination are water, light, soil, and temperature?

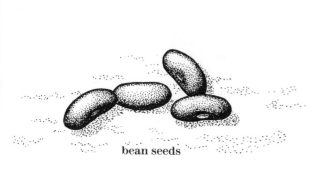

bean seeds

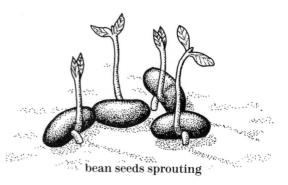

bean seeds sprouting

ACTIVITY 1

Finding the Conditions for Germination

In this activity, you will need to divide your class into four groups. Each group will do a test for one of the four conditions.

Group 1: light
Group 2: water
Group 3: soil
Group 4: temperature

Materials

8 250-mL beakers (or clean plastic glasses)
8 paper towels
32 bean seeds
6 thermometers
enough garden soil to fill *one* beaker to a height of 3 cm

Procedure

Group 1

1. In a three-column table, make the headings *Condition*, *Prediction*, and *Results*.
2. Under the heading *Condition*, list the items for which the testing is being carried out. For Group 1 the items are
   a) *light present*
   b) *light absent*
3. Predict the importance of each condition to the germination of seeds. Record this prediction as *necessary*, *unnecessary*, or *no effect*.
4. Roll two paper towels into the shape of a cylinder. Place one inside each beaker as shown here.

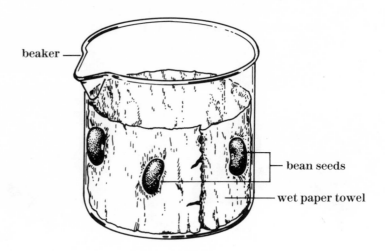

beaker —
bean seeds
wet paper towel

5. Pour water into each beaker to a height of 1 cm.

6. Place four bean seeds between the paper towel and the wall of each beaker. Separate the seeds from each other as much as possible. Insert a thermometer between the paper towel and the wall of the beaker.

7. Place one beaker in a dark cupboard. Label it as the *test beaker*. Place the other beaker in a lighted area. Label it as the *control beaker*.

8. Over the next week, observe and record on a daily basis what you see happening in each beaker. If desired, continue your observations for another week.

9. During the observation period, ensure that conditions of *moisture* and *temperature* remain the same for each beaker.

10. On the basis of your observations, complete the *Results* column of the table you made in step 1. Record *necessary*, *unnecessary*, or *no effect*.

11. Compare your predictions and results with those of the other groups.

Group 2

1. Substituting the conditions *water present*, *water absent*, do steps 1 through 4 as indicated for Group 1.

2. Pour water into one beaker to a height of 1 cm. Label this beaker as the *control beaker*. Label the other one as the *test beaker*.

3. Ensuring that conditions of *light* and *temperature* remain the same for each beaker, do step 6 and steps 8, 10, and 11, as indicated for Group 1. Omit steps 5, 7, and 9.

In hydroponic gardening, plants are grown in water with nutrients added.

Group 3

1. Substituting the conditions *soil present*, *soil absent*, do steps 1 through 6 as indicated in Group 1.
2. In one beaker, place some of the soil in the bottom and the rest around the seeds. Label this beaker as the *control beaker*. Label the other one as the *test beaker*.
3. Ensuring that conditions of *moisture*, *temperature*, and *light* remain the same for each beaker, repeat steps 8, 10 and 11, as indicated for Group 1. Omit steps 7 and 9.

Group 4

1. Substituting the conditions *at room temperature*, *in the refrigerator*, do steps 1 through 6 as indicated for Group 1.
2. Place one beaker in the refrigerator. Label this beaker as the *test beaker*. Label the other one as the *control beaker* and place it in a dark cupboard.
3. Ensuring that conditions of *moisture* and *light* remain the same for each beaker, repeat steps 8, 10, and 11, as indicated for Group 1. Omit steps 7 and 9.

Discussion

1. By placing pairs of beakers under different conditions, you have performed what is called a **controlled experiment**. What do you think it means when an experiment is controlled? Why is it useful to do controlled experiments?
2. Based on class results, what conditions do you think are needed for seed germination?
3. If you placed some seeds in the refrigerator, what else, other than temperature, could have affected your results?
4. Predict whether germinated seeds need light to keep growing.

Extension

1. Take your germinated seeds home and watch them grow. Observe their progress over a few weeks. How do they change?
2. Using only water with nutrients added, continue to grow some germinated seeds. The science of growing plants in water with nutrients added is called **hydroponics**.
3. Research the use of hydroponics for the production of plants as a source of food.

Taking a Closer Look at a Seed

In this activity, you will examine in detail the structures that make up a seed.

Materials

bean seed half
magnifying lens

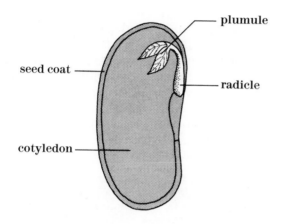

Procedure

1. Observe the bean seed half with the magnifying lens. As you do so, try to locate and identify the structures shown in this diagram.

Discussion

1. Which of the four structures you observed within the bean seed was the largest? the smallest?

Seeds: Their Structure and Function

Each of the four structures of a seed has a special function.
    The **seed coat** is very important for the seed's survival before germination. This tough structure protects the seed from damage and water loss. Germination will only occur if

the seed's environment becomes wet enough and warm enough. The seed can wait for a long time before germination. When ancient Egyptian kings died, seeds were often placed in their tombs with them. Scientists have recovered such seeds, which are thousands of years old, and have grown plants from them.

After germination, the **radicle** and the **plumule** spring to life. The radicle grows to form the beginning of a root, while the plumule develops into a stem.

Meanwhile, the **cotyledons** are a stored source of food for the developing root and stem. A young plant has begun its life. But the cotyledons can only provide food for a short time. By the time the food supply stored in them runs out, the young plant needs to be able to make food on its own. Once a plant can make food for itself, it can begin to grow.

Certain conditions are necessary to this growth. Light, water, temperature, and chemical nutrients are important to plant growth. It is usually the soil that provides a source of chemical nutrients.

Some of these conditions, however, may be more, or less, important to one plant than to another. For example, some plants need much more water than the bean plant does. Other

The necessity for the right amount of water for a plant to be healthy is obvious from this picture. The plant on the left has been overwatered, the one in the centre has been underwatered, and the one on the right has been given the right amount of water.

plants need less. The same is true for the other three conditions. The kind or amount of water, light, soil, and temperature necessary to the growth of a palm tree differs from that necessary to the growth of a maple tree.

Questions

1. What are the environmental conditions necessary in these cases?
   a) both seed germination and plant growth
   b) plant growth, but not seed germination
2. List the four major structures of a seed and the function of each one.
3. If the soil in which a plant is located does not have enough nutrients, what can be done to increase the amount of nutrients?
4. Is a seed alive? Explain your answer.

The major structures of a mature plant are called **organs**. There are five important ones: roots, leaves, stems, flowers, and seeds. You have already examined seeds. You will now look, in turn, at the structure and the function of each of the other four main organs.

8.2

Structures of a Plant and What They Do

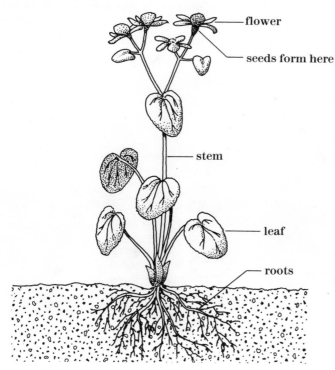

flower

seeds form here

stem

leaf

roots

The Root: Anchor and Nourisher

Plants, like all other living things, need water in order to survive. A vital function of roots is to absorb water from the soil. Water intake is important for a number of reasons. Chemical nutrients from the soil dissolve in water and enter the plant through the roots. Water is one of the substances used in photosynthesis. Water is also an important component of plant cells.

Different kinds of plants need different amounts of water. For example, a plant rooted in the bottom of a river needs a lot of water. A desert plant, such as a cactus, can survive on much less water. You might think that a cactus would do better with plenty of moisture. But in fact, excess water causes the cactus root to rot, killing the plant. What would happen if a plant that normally was rooted in wet soil was planted in the desert?

In addition to absorbing water and nutrients, roots act as an organ of food storage. In chapter 2, you learned that plants carry out photosynthesis. **Glucose** is one product of photosynthesis. It is one of the most important foods used by plants and animals. When a plant makes more glucose than it needs, it converts this extra glucose to another substance, called **starch**.

This food reserve is often useful to humans as well. The carrot is an example of a root that you use for food. The carrot root is convenient as a food because it has one major, central part. Such roots are called **tap roots**. This type of root often grows very deep in the soil and can usually reach more water than other roots.

Why are some of the banyan tree's roots above ground?

What type of root do you think cactus plants have?

Tapioca is made from the starchy cassava root.

If you have ever tried to pull out dandelions from a lawn, or carrots from a garden, you know that roots anchor plants in the ground. Plants cannot normally move from one place to another like most animals can. The roots of most plants anchor them so that they will not be washed away during heavy rain, or uprooted by severe winds.

Other plants, such as grasses, have roots that branch out into the soil in all directions. These are called **fibrous roots**. The network of roots produced by grasses can be important in holding surface soil in place. For this reason, grasses are often used to prevent soil from being washed away by water on slopes.

What type of roots do you think sea oats have?

Grasses have fibrous roots.

Leaves: The Food Makers

As you have learned, the food supply in the cotyledons is limited. When the food in the cotyledons is used up, the plant must begin to produce its own food. It does so in its leaves through photosynthesis.

You remember from chapter 2 that green plant cells contain structures called chloroplastids. The chloroplastids in plant cells contain the substance **chlorophyll**. Chlorophyll is the substance that gives plants their green color. Only in the presence of chlorophyll and enough light is photosynthesis possible. The chlorophyll and light act to convert carbon dioxide and water into **glucose** and oxygen and water. Photosynthesis is an example of energy conversion. Light energy is converted into chemical energy that is stored in glucose and starch.

leaf
containing
chlorophyll
light energy ⟶ chemical energy

Photosynthesis involves a chemical reaction in which carbon dioxide and water are changed into glucose and oxygen and water.

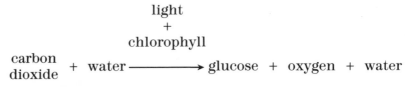

light
+
chlorophyll
carbon dioxide + water ⟶ glucose + oxygen + water

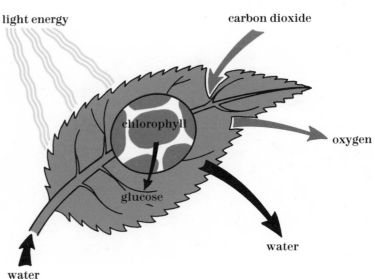

Photosynthesis

Evidence of Photosynthesis in Leaves

How could you make sure that it is the leaves of plants that are responsible for photosynthesis? Since you cannot observe photosynthesis, you must use other evidence to infer that it is taking place.

As two pieces of evidence, consider the *color* and the *position* of leaves. You know that leaves are green and chlorophyll is green. You also know that photosynthesis requires light. The leaves of plants are located so that light can reach them.

As a third piece of evidence, consider that glucose is a product of photosynthesis. The presence of glucose in leaves would suggest that photosynthesis happens in leaves. Since plants change glucose into starch, the presence of starch would

If only one light source is available, plants will bend toward it.

indicate that photosynthesis has occurred.

Water is also a product of photosynthesis. The escape of water through a plant's leaves would therefore be a fourth piece of evidence.

In the activity and demonstration that follow, you will examine these last two kinds of evidence for photosynthesis in the leaves of a plant.

ACTIVITY 3   Looking for Starch in a Leaf

In this activity, you will try to show that starch can be found in leaves.

Materials

bean leaves or geranium leaves
250-mL beaker half filled with water
alcohol burner (or other source of heat)
metal tongs
about 50 mL of alcohol in 250-mL beaker
petri dish or saucer
iodine solution
eyedropper
safety goggles

Procedure

1. Make a table like the one below.

Appearance of Leaf	Color	Other Observations
picked from plant		
after boiling		
in alcohol		
on petri dish		
with iodine added		

2. Pick one healthy leaf from the plant. Observe and record the appearance of the leaf.
3. With tongs, place the leaf in the boiling water for 5 min. *Wear safety goggles*. Observe and record the leaf's appearance.
4. With tongs, remove the leaf from the water and place it in the beaker of alcohol. Observe and record the leaf's appearance. *Alcohol is highly flammable. Keep it away from an open flame*.

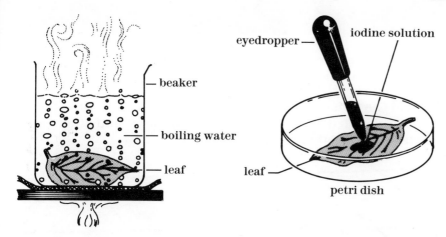

5. After 5 min, remove the leaf from the alcohol and place it on a petri dish. Observe and record the leaf's appearance.
6. Observe the color of the iodine solution in the small bottle. Then place four or five drops of iodine solution on the middle of the leaf. Observe and record the leaf's appearance.

Discussion

1. Why did the alcohol change in color?
2. What was the purpose of boiling the leaf?
3. As you learned in chapter 6, some chemicals change color when they come into contact with others. These chemical tests can be useful in identifying substances. What substance did you use as a chemical in this activity to test for starch? What change did you observe? What can you infer from this change?

Cabbage leaves provide many nutrients for humans and animals.

The Field and the Greenhouse

Most food plants, such as wheat or apple trees, can be grown in fields or orchards. But raising crops is a hazardous business for farmers because some factors, such as the weather, are beyond the farmer's control. Wind, hail, early frost, drought, or flooding can destroy crops. Insects, diseases, and other hazards can also do serious damage.

Plants in greenhouses are protected from many hazards and can be grown year-round.

Greenhouses are a way to avoid the unpredictability of outdoor environments. Using technology, humans can create indoor greenhouse environments that are ideal for any desired plant. But it would be impractical to grow all our food plants indoors. Creating artificial environments is expensive, and this makes the food grown in greenhouses more expensive.

But there are important advantages to growing some foods in greenhouses. A greenhouse makes it possible to grow food plants in the middle of winter, decreasing our dependence on food imported from other countries. Crops that grow outdoors can be given a head start in a greenhouse, then transplanted to the field. This practice can compensate for cool climates with short growing seasons.

A baby forest is growing some 1402 m below the ground, in a mine shaft at the International Nickel Company in Sudbury, Ontario. Using special lighting, heating, and watering systems, tiny pine seedlings are grown underground during the winter and then replanted above ground in the summer. The same system has been used to grow vegetables.

Even so, many food plants must still be grown outdoors during a short growing season. To improve the quality of such crops, scientists combine the good characteristics of two plants into one new plant. The resulting plant is called a *hybrid*.

A good example of a hybrid is the grain plant *triticale*. This grain is a hybrid of durum wheat and rye. Triticale plants are hardy, much like rye. Triticale grain has very desirable characteristics for making flour, much like durum wheat. Using hybrids, farmers are able to make the most of their various field and orchard environments.

Connections

DEMONSTRATION 1

Looking for Evidence of Water Loss in Leaves

In this demonstration, you will look for evidence of the escape of water from the leaves of a plant.

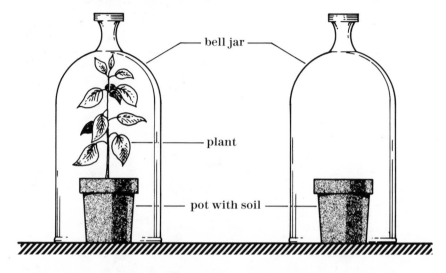

1. Two bell jars are set up. Inside one is a healthy plant in a pot of soil. Inside the other bell jar is only a pot of soil.
2. The bell jars are left for several days in a lighted area.
3. Inside the top surface of the bell jar containing the plant, water droplets are observed. Inside the other bell jar, no droplets are observed.

Discussion

1. Explain why there were water droplets inside one bell jar, but not the other.
2. Was the formation of water droplets on the inside of the bell jar a physical change or a chemical change?

Control of Water Loss in Leaves

As you observed in Demonstration 1, leaves give off water. This process of water loss is called **transpiration**. It takes place through small openings in the leaves called **stomata**. A single opening is called a **stoma**.

Transpiration occurs more quickly in some plants than in others. Plants that grow in very dry environments cannot afford to give off much water. The presence of fewer stomata in these plants lowers the amount of transpiration that occurs.

Observing Stomata

In this activity, you will observe a leaf and see how it controls water loss.

Materials

microscope
prepared slide of leaf undersurface

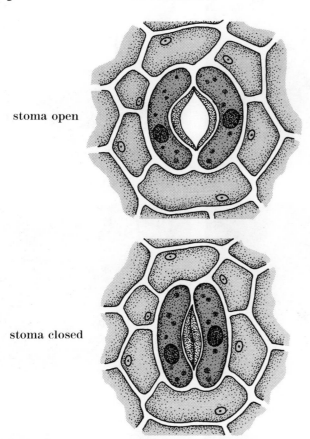

stoma open

stoma closed

Procedure

1. Review Activity 2 in chapter 2 on page 37.
2. Obtain a prepared slide of the undersurface of a leaf from your teacher.
3. Observe the leaf using the low-power objective lens.
4. Observe the leaf using the medium-power objective lens. Look for a number of holes in the leaf. Make a sketch of your observations.
5. Observe the leaf using the high-power objective lens. Try to sketch more details of your observations.

The Stem: Pathway for Nutrients

The stem is the plant organ that connects the roots to the leaves and flowers. There are many different types of stems. Some are soft and fleshy, others are hard and rough. Some stand straight up, others lie along the ground.

a) Bean plants: soft, fleshy stem

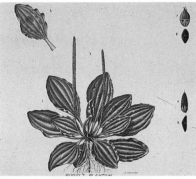
b) Plantain: fleshy stem

c) Redwood trees: hard, rough, upright stem

d) Vines: woody stems lie along the ground, need support to grow upright

e) Cacti plants: soft, erect stem

f) Lily pads: soft, fleshy, upright stem

Examples of different types of stems

What effect do you think that the shade created by these trees will have on young trees just beginning their growth?

The height of a plant usually depends on the length of its stem. If it is competing with other plants for sunlight, a plant with a long stem has an advantage. With more sunlight reaching its leaves, it can photosynthesize more food and grow more quickly.

The stem has another very important function. In order to carry out photosynthesis, the leaves need water and chemical nutrients from the soil. The stem is the pathway that carries these substances from the roots to the leaves and flowers.

This pathway also works in the other direction. As you learned earlier, the roots store food in the form of starch. This food, which is produced in the leaves, travels through the stem to the roots for storage. The stem not only carries the nutrients to the leaves, but it also carries glucose from the leaves. In the roots, glucose is changed to starch.

DEMONSTRATION 2

Observing the Function of a Stem

In this demonstration, you will look for evidence that a stem carries substances to the leaves and flowers.

1. Three white carnations are placed in beakers of differently colored water.
2. The beakers are left overnight.
3. The flower of each carnation has absorbed the color of the liquid in which it was placed.

Discussion

1. What caused the color change in the carnations?

Extension

1. Obtain some plant roots, stems, or leaves. Grow them in water. When they are mature enough, transplant them into soil.

These carnations, originally white, have taken on the color of the dyed water in which they were placed. How can you explain this?

Flowers: The Seed Makers

When a plant reaches maturity, the flower produces seeds to make more plants. In this diagram, you can see some of the structures of a typical flower.

Apple Blossom

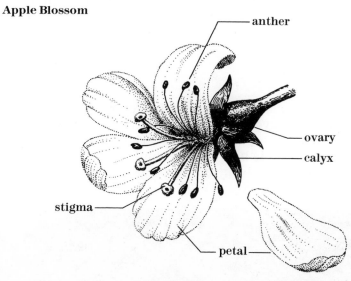

The seeds develop in the flower's ovary. When you eat an apple, for example, look at the apple core. The end of the core that is opposite to the stem is where the petals of the flower used to be. The fleshy part of the apple grew around the ovary after the seeds began to develop. You might find the seeds are a nuisance, but they are very important for apple trees.

Fruit

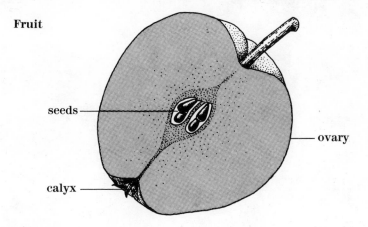

Seeds are not the only means that plants have for reproducing themselves. You can sometimes grow a new plant from a single root, stem, or leaf.

Questions

1. In which part(s) of a plant is food produced? stored?
2. a) In what form is the food stored?
   b) How does this food get from where it is made to where it is stored?
3. What are the three products of photosynthesis?
4. From what four kinds of evidence can you infer that photosynthesis takes place in leaves?
5. From which part(s) of a plant can new plants be produced?

8.3

Plants in Your Life

Plants affect your life in a wide variety of ways. Photosynthesis produces the oxygen that you breathe. Plants provide you with food, fuel, fibres, drugs, and a variety of other useful substances. They provide habitats for wildlife. They even help to make the world more beautiful, especially when flowers are in bloom.

In addition to providing so many things that are vital for life, plants help to make the world more beautiful.

Drugs

The drug digitalis is extracted from the leaves of the foxglove plant. Digitalis is useful in treating certain kinds of heart disease.

The drug digitalis is obtained from foxglove.

Another drug, atropine, is extracted from the roots of the belladonna plant. Belladonna is commonly known as deadly nightshade. In fact, the drug atropine is fatal in large amounts. But in small doses, atropine can be used in treating a variety of illnesses.

Atropine is extracted from the roots of the belladonna (Deadly Nightshade) plant.

Caffeine is a drug you may be familiar with. It is found in coffee beans, cocoa beans, and tea leaves. Among other things, caffeine stimulates your nervous system and helps to prevent drowsiness. But too much coffee, tea, or chocolate can make you tense and jumpy.

a) Evening primrose

b) Wild violets

c) Assortment of herbs, including camomile, dandelions, and green onions that have gone to seed

Plants have been used for medicinal purposes or as food for centuries, including such pretty, flowering plants as primroses and violets and more common ones such as green onions.

Lumber and Fuel

Canada is rich in forests, which provide a variety of useful materials. Wood is still one of the most useful materials we have for construction. Firewood has become less important as a fuel in recent decades, but it is still reliable and versatile.

Wood is used in the making of paper.

Oils

Some plant seeds contain useful oils. A common example is palm oil, which is extracted from the seeds of palm trees. This oil is used in the making of soaps. The oil of sunflowers, corn, olives, or peanuts is widely used for frying or for salad dressings.

The oil of the canola plant is used as cooking oil, fuel, and in making soap.

Fibre

Plants such as cotton and flax are useful in manufacturing fabrics. In cotton plants, the white fibres of the cotton boll surround the cotton seeds. The fibres used in the making of linen come from the stem of the flax plant.

Flax plants are used in the making of clothing.

Rag-and-bone men used to roam the streets of the cities collecting bones that were then used to make fertilizer and rags that were used in the manufacture of paper.

Food

You depend on plants for all of your food. When you eat a hamburger, you know that it includes plant materials from wheat, lettuce, and tomatoes. But even the meat could not have been produced without plants.

Plants were necessary to produce the ingredients of this hamburger.

What is a Weed?

Some people think of dandelions as weeds, but some think of them as flowers. Some people even think they are tasty in salads. Whether you think of a plant as a weed depends on your point of view. In general, a weed is a plant that is growing where it is not wanted. Plants such as ragweed are often unwanted. Many people are allergic to ragweed pollen grains.

Sneezing is one of the common symptoms of an allergy. What are some of the other symptoms?

Then and Now

Medicinal Uses of Plants

Then

The use of plants for medicinal purposes is an ancient practice. Using trial and error, early human tribes discovered which plants were edible and which had medicinal properties. Some plant materials were found to be useful for such purposes as healing cuts or other injuries. North American Indians chewed willow twigs to reduce aches and pains. The willow contains salicylic acid, from which aspirin is made today.

In the early civilizations of Asia and Europe, doctors prescribed potions, ointments, and plasters made of plant substances. Such plants often are called herbs. Many early doctors believed that a plant's shape or natural markings indicated the way in which it should be used. Some herbs were thought to have magical properties in addition to their actual medicinal ones. About 400 a ago, Li Shih-chen wrote a 52-volume encyclopedia of ancient Chinese herbal remedies. Many of them probably were first used some 5000 a ago.

This little North American Indian boy is enjoying a drink of birch sap from a cup made of birch bark. The sap is sweet tasting.

Now

In many parts of the world, folk medicine based on plant materials continues even today. Many such plant substances have been shown to have valuable medicinal properties. The drug ephedrine, used in treating asthma, comes from the plant mahuang (*Ephedra vulgaris*), which has been used in China for at least 4000 a. A drug used in high blood pressure treatment, reserpine, comes from a Chinese plant called *Rauwolfia*.

At the University of Alberta, the value of other ancient Chinese medicines is being tested. Jinan University in China is providing the herb samples, along with Chinese experts to work on the project. They are working with Alberta scientist Peter Pang, who arranged the agreement.

"Herbs do work," says Dr. Pang, "and unlike many drugs, they often don't have serious side effects." His goal is to subject these herbs to "thorough, systematic, scientific analysis to find out what they do and how they do it."

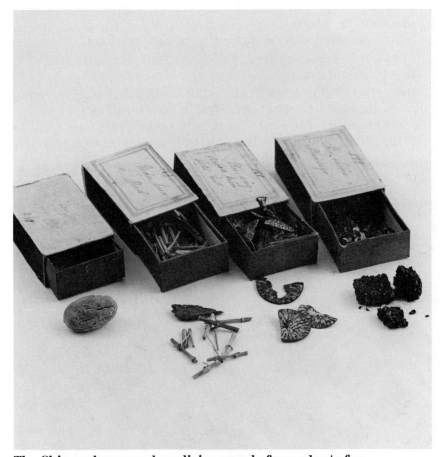

The Chinese have used medicines made from plants for thousands of years. The above, stored in matchboxes are nutmeg, ephedra, areca nuts, and plantago.

ACTIVITY 5

Lunching and Munching on Plants

In this activity, you will explore different ways in which plants can be used in foods.

Materials

foods made from plants

Procedure

1. Make a table like the one below.

Plant	Country of Origin	Parts Used for Food

2. Go to a grocery store and buy any food or foods made from plants. Note which of the five major parts of the plant or plants are used as food. Record your observations.
3. Find out the country from which the food came. Record this information.
4. Bring the food to class in any edible or drinkable form you wish. Be sure that what you bring is different from, or at least prepared differently from, what your classmates bring. Share your plant lunch with your classmates.

In this picture, which part of the plants is used for food?

Discussion

1. Compare your table of observations with those of your classmates. Which part of plants seem to be most commonly used as food?
2. Which parts of your plant or plants are not edible? Why?
3. Where did your plant come from? Why do you think it was grown there?

Extension

1. Make a poster showing examples of how plants are used for drugs, clothing, food, or leisure.

Questions

1. Give four examples of how plants are used in your life.
2. For each example, name three plants that are used in this way.

Summary

Germination is the first stage in the development of a plant. Sufficient water and temperature are required for germination. Sufficient water, temperature, light, and nutrients are required for growth.

A germinated seed has four major parts. These are the seed coat, cotyledons, plumule, and radicle.

A mature plant has five major parts. These are the roots, leaves, stem, flowers, and seeds.

Roots anchor the plant in the soil and absorb water and nutrients.

Leaves are the site of photosynthesis. They release water vapor through the stomata. Photosynthesis uses carbon dioxide and water, in the presence of light and chlorophyll, to produce glucose, oxygen, and water. The leaves transform this glucose into starch. The leaves also release water through their stomata.

Stems carry nutrients from the roots to the leaves and flowers, and carry food from the leaves to the roots for storage.

Flowers produce seeds inside the ovary. Plants can reproduce by means of seeds. They can also reproduce using other plant parts, such as roots, stems, and leaves.

Plants play a vital role in your life. They are used in many ways. Drugs, fuel, fibre, and food are some of these ways.

Chapter Questions

Remember

1. **a)** List the five major organs of a plant.
   b) List the function(s) of each one.
2. Which of the statements below are true? Which are false? Rewrite the false statements to make them true.
   a) The presence of light is a necessary condition for both the germination of seeds and the growth of plants.
   b) In controlling experiments, different conditions are created for each of the two samples tested.
   c) Food is made in the leaves of plants.
   d) The plumule of a seed develops into the stem of a mature plant.
   e) All plants have stems that stand upright.
   f) All food energy used by plants and animals comes either directly or indirectly from photosynthesis.
   g) The part of the plant which gives off water is the flower.
   h) The seed is the only part of a plant from which a new plant can ever be created.
   i) The oils of plants have no practical uses.

Think

1. Why do animals need plants?
2. Could a rosebush ever be called a weed?

The pitcher plant traps insects. Why does it do this?

3. Research the plant-growing conditions that exist on northern Canada's tundra. Make a list of these conditions. Do further research to find out what plants can grow under these conditions.

Dream

1. Try to imagine what your neighborhood would be like if there were no plants.
2. If you were going to grow plants on a spaceship, what kind of plants would you choose? Consider each plant's value as a food, oxygen producer, or other resource.

Various plants were grown in space in the manned spacecraft Apollo 12.

Decide

1. In southern Ontario, the growing of tobacco plants to make cigarettes is a major source of income for tobacco farmers. However, there is very convincing medical evidence that cigarette smoking is a serious health hazard. How might governments encourage tobacco growers to cultivate other crops in place of tobacco plants?

9

Independent Investigation

How can you tell the age of a rock? How do ants find food at a picnic? How does a stereo speaker work?

The world around you is an endless source of questions. When you try to answer these questions you are doing science.

Science is not just a lot of facts about the world. It is a process of asking questions and trying to find the best answers to those questions. But how do you use science to satisfy your curiosity? That is what this chapter is about—investigating on your own.

How do you start your own investigation? Your class activities are organized in a step-by-step procedure. An independent investigation requires the same type of approach. This figure will help you ask the right questions at the right time. Each of the five steps will be described in detail in the following sections of this chapter.

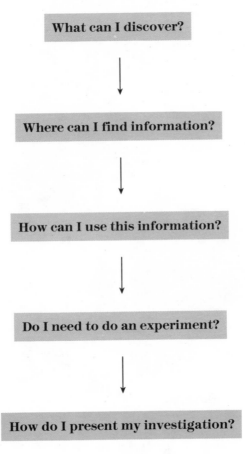

There are several ways to decide what you want to discover. You can begin by asking yourself a question like *What am I interested in?*

What can I discover?

What am I interested in?

Consider some subjects that interest you. These will be very general subjects. Here are some examples.

living things   atmosphere
technology   oceans
Earth   space

Suppose that you are interested in technology. Now you need to pick a more specific topic within this general subject. This topic should be one that you already know something about.

What am I familiar with?

Your own experience will tell you what you are familiar with. What product of technology have you seen before and wondered about? If you pick something familiar to you, you will understand it more easily. If you choose something unfamiliar, you might just copy words that you do not understand. At the same time, you should choose a topic that is not too complicated. If it is, you again will be forced just to copy words.

After you have chosen a topic, you need to be even more specific. You have to ask a question about a single aspect of your topic.

What specific question can I ask?

Perhaps you are interested in music. You probably listen to the stereo at home, and you are familiar with it. You might decide to investigate how it works. What question should you try to answer?

Specific questions have specific answers. Discovering how a speaker works will be much easier than finding out how the whole system works. There are fewer things to investigate. But even a speaker is quite complicated. Be even more specific. You may want to investigate only one of the following questions.

- How does a speaker produce sounds?
- Why are some speakers larger than others?
- How does the speaker cabinet affect the sound?

Can I make a hypothesis?

How do you know if your question is specific enough? Try to suggest or guess more than one possible answer. State each possible answer in the form of a hypothesis. If the answer is obvious, then the question does not need further investigation.

Questions

1. For each of the general subjects mentioned on page 249, pick a topic, ask a specific question about it, and make a hypothesis.

You now have a specific question. Where do you find information to answer it? Suppose your question was *How do speakers work?* There are several possible sources of information. Three of these sources are *what you already know about it*, *what you can read about it*, and *who you can talk to about it*.

Where can I find information?

What do I already know?

Your own experiences may be a useful source of information. Even if you know little about the topic you are investigating, this information will still help guide your search for the answer.

What can I read?

First, you should get some general information. A reference book, such as an encyclopedia, is a source of information. However, an encyclopedia might not give enough detailed information about your topic. If you are unable to find enough information, ask your teacher or librarian for help. In fact, you may decide to change the specific question that you are trying to answer when you learn something new about the topic.

Now you will need more detailed information about the question *How do speakers work?* But where will you look? A library will have books listed under the title *Speakers*, but there may not be many. Remember that this topic is part of a more general subject. You might find good information under several other titles such as *Sound*, *Magnets*, or *Electricity*.

You might even need to look under a more general title. All of these topics are part of *physics*. Any physics book might have more information for you. Remember to use the index and the table of contents to help find the information that you need.

Magazines will also have articles that are useful. But be careful. Many books and magazines may be too complicated. If they use too much technical language, avoid them. A librarian can help you find what you need. Some libraries might have access to information stored in computers. Again, the librarian can help you.

Use more than one book or article as a source of information. Write down the title, author, and page number when you find information you can use. Make notes and sketches of what you find.

Who can I talk to?

If you are having trouble finding or understanding information about your topic, perhaps there is someone who can give you advice.

Anyone who repairs, sells, or works with speakers might be able to help. Clubs are also a good place to look. Take advantage of experts around you. They are often happy to help. But never use them in place of your own work.

Case Study

Chance Discoveries in Science

Usually, scientists experiment to test the predictions of a theory. Often, they are simply interested in observing something under new conditions. In either case, they already suspect what they will see.

Like you, scientists can be so involved in looking for what they expect to see that they miss the unexpected. But sooner or later, someone will notice an unexpected observation and recognize its importance. This is called a chance discovery.

In 1928, in England, Alexander Fleming was investigating ways to help the body fight bacterial infections. To do this, he had to prepare cultures of bacteria. Each culture had to be one pure strain of bacteria. No other organisms could be present.

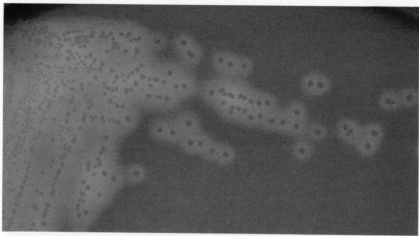

This is a pure culture of strep throat bacteria. Cultures are often ruined by the growth of unwanted moulds.

This is not always easy to do. Often, unwanted moulds grow as well. These ruin the culture and it must be thrown away.

In a busy laboratory, the ruined cultures are often set aside to be thrown out later. This is what Fleming did on the day that he discovered penicillin. Certainly, others had done it before him.

Here is where chance played a part. In one ruined culture, a mould known as *penicillium* had grown. Before the ruined cultures were destroyed, Fleming happened to look at this particular one. He noticed a curious effect. Bacteria were not growing near the mould. This would never have been observed if the cultures had been destroyed immediately.

Perhaps other scientists had noticed this effect before. But no one before Fleming realized its importance. The mould was producing a material that killed bacteria.

Although it took twelve more years of work for other scientists to purify the antibiotic penicillin, it was Fleming's curiosity that made it possible. It is ironic that he found what he was looking for in a ruined experiment.

Questions

Read more about the discovery made by Alexander Fleming and answer these questions.
1. Describe the discovery he made.
2. Was the discovery the result of experimentation?
3. Did the discovery have a practical value to society?
4. If possible, explain how the scientist became interested in the problem.
5. Explain the way in which the discovery was made. Was it a chance discovery?

9.3

How can I use my information?

By now, you have gathered a lot of information. Use your information to test each of your hypotheses. Are any of your hypotheses supported by your information? These are **valid hypotheses**. Are any of your hypotheses contradicted by your information? These are **invalid hypotheses**. Now consider your valid hypotheses only. Reject your invalid ones. If none of your hypotheses are valid, you will have to make new ones. If you have found a valid hypothesis, you might be ready to present your information.

9.4

Do I need to do an experiment?

For some hypotheses, you might not find enough information in books. To test the validity of such hypotheses, you may need to do an experiment.

You may want to do an experiment, even though your hypothesis is supported by what you have read. Information in a book is rarely as dramatically convincing as experimental proof. Doing an experiment also gives you hands-on experience and can be a lot of fun.

How can I design an experiment?

Start with a specific problem. Your problem should be stated in the form of a question.

Make more than one hypothesis about the answer. These hypotheses give you a basis from which to start your experiment.

Suppose you are considering the effect of different colors of light on plants. Your question might be *Which color of light is best for the growth of plants?*

You already know that chlorophyll is green. Therefore, you might hypothesize that *since chlorophyll is green, green is the best color for growth*. But you also know that infrared lamps are used for keeping things warm. So you might also hypothesize that *since infrared lamps keep things warm, red is the best color for growth*.

Your next step will be to choose methods and materials to test your hypotheses.

Experiments could continue until every condition that affects the question has been examined. Each experiment poses new questions. Your decision to stop an experiment might depend on the time and equipment available. It is difficult to find complete answers and sometimes you may never find them.

What methods and materials should I use?

You must design your experiment to provide for each of the conditions included in your hypothesis. To test for the best color of light for plant growth, you will vary the color of the light.

You must design your experiment to ensure that the following experimental conditions are constant: the amount of light, the length of time each plant is grown, the type of seed, the kind of potting soil, the size and shape of the containers. Grow one set of plants under unfiltered white light. Use this set of plants to make comparisons with the other sets of plants.

To make it clear what materials and methods you will use, *draw a labelled diagram* of the set-up for your experiment. You should also *list the steps of your procedure*.

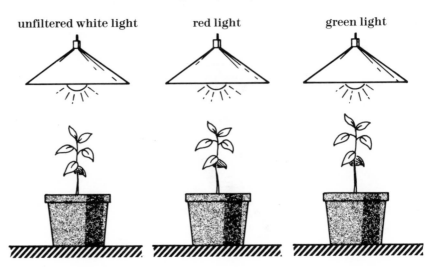

unfiltered white light   red light   green light

How do I record observations?

You will need to record both the total mass of the plants and the color of light used in each group. Do not forget to record information such as the number of days the plants were allowed to grow, even if this information is the same for all the plants. In other words, record all experimental conditions.

It is helpful to organize your observations in the form of a table.

Color of Light Used	Time Grown (days)	Number of Seeds Planted	Number of Seeds Sprouted	Total Mass of Plants (grams)
white	21	20	14	276
red	21	20	12	325
green	21	20	9	97

You can also present your results in the form of a graph. When you use a graph, you are presenting information in a visual form. This is often the easiest form to understand.

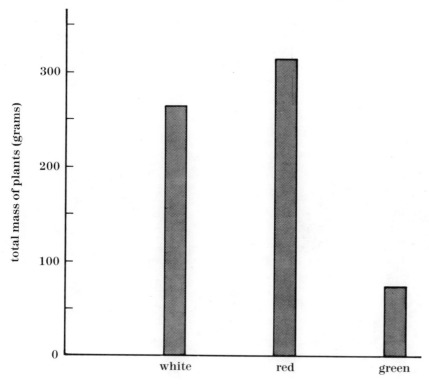

How do I make a conclusion?

To make a conclusion, you must analyse the observations you have recorded. Then, based on your analysis, state the answer to your question. Your statement might be very similar to one of your hypotheses. If you were testing for the effect of different colors of light on plant growth, your conclusion might be written as *red is the best color of light for plant growth*.

Your conclusion might include new questions for further investigation. For example, you might ask, *how is light energy related to color*?

Then and Now

The Changing Role of Observation in Science

Galileo Galilei was one of the first scientists to perform careful experiments.

Then

Aristotle and other Greek scientists observed the world around them and formed ideas to explain their observations. Once they formed an idea, they did not believe it was necessary to test the idea by making further observations.

For example, Aristotle observed light objects, such as feathers, and heavy objects, such as rocks, falling to the ground. He noticed that the rocks fell to the ground faster than did the feathers. Aristotle formed the idea that the heavier an object is, the faster it will fall. He did not consider it necessary to test this prediction by performing experiments and making further observations.

Another of Aristotle's ideas was that women had fewer teeth than men. He may have based this idea on the observation that female horses usually have four teeth fewer than male horses. However, Aristotle never actually counted teeth in men and women to confirm this theory.

Aristotle's ideas were unchallenged for some 2000 a. Not until the seventeenth century was the importance of using experiments to test ideas recognized.

Galileo (1564–1642) was one of the first scientists to challenge Aristotle's authority. According to a popular story, Galileo dropped a cannonball and a small pebble from the Leaning Tower of Pisa to test Aristotle's theory about falling objects. He found that both objects reached the ground at the same time. This and later experiments completely disproved Aristotle's theory.

Now

Many scientific theories have been developed to explain observations. For example, there are theories of evolutions, theories to explain the structure of matter, and theories to explain the origin of the universe. Scientific theories are not facts. They are ideas formulated to explain observations.

Theories are not perfect and they do not always explain all observations. If new observations and experiments do not agree with a scientific theory, then the theory must be changed. Sometimes even a modified theory cannot explain the facts and the theory must be rejected. Then a new theory must be formed to explain the observations.

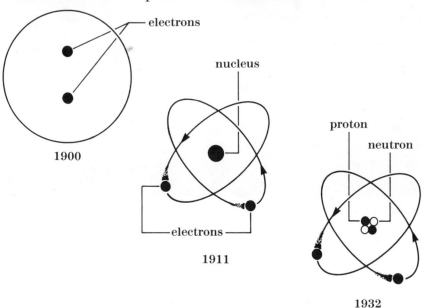

No one has ever seen a helium atom. However, based on experiments done by the year 1900, scientists had some idea of its structure. This model has continued to change as new experiments were done, resulting in 1932 in the final drawing shown above. However, even this drawing does not agree completely with all experiments.

9.5

How do I present my investigation?

Once you have information supporting your hypothesis or hypotheses, you will want to share your information.

How can I explain it to someone else?

There are several ways to present your information to others. Each way helps you to test your understanding and provides good experience in communication.

A class presentation is a good way to explain your investigation.

One way to present information is to write an essay. If you do so, you must answer all possible questions in a clear and organized manner.

You may prefer a class presentation. It will give you experience in speaking to a large group. Because there are many people listening to you, many different questions may be asked.

If you are competitive or simply like a challenge, enter a science fair. A science fair can be an excellent test of your understanding and your ability to communicate. In addition, someone very knowledgeable about your topic will judge your presentation.

How do I present a project at a science fair?

There are five kinds of projects presented at a science fair, *information only*, *collected specimens*, *working models*, *partial experiments*, and *complete experiments*.

Presentation of an Information Only Project

This choice is the simplest kind of project. It is similar to doing an essay or chart. The information can be in the form of written description, labelled diagrams, calculations, or graphs. The best presentation would use most or all of these forms.

Here are some things that you should do in a presentation of an information only project.

1. Organize carefully.
2. Use many titles.
3. Plan the flow of the information.
4. Be as brief as possible.
5. Use color.
6. Make everything large and easy to read.
7. Include your sources of information.

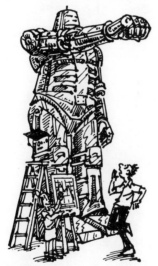

Here are some things you should *not* do.

1. Crowd your information.
2. Print long descriptions.
3. Leave out important information.
4. Assume that the viewer knows anything about your topic.
5. Use technical words without explanation.

Making

Science in Many Cultures

In 1453, a German jeweller, Johannes Gutenberg printed the first book in the Western world. In the same century, western Europe was introduced to gunpowder and magnetized needles that could be used as compasses. Many historians believe that the knowledge that led to the use of these objects was brought from China by traders or missionaries.

These discoveries and countless others from many cultures were essential in the development of what is now called modern science.

The valley of the Tigris and Euphrates Rivers, today part of Iraq and Iran, has been the home of various cultures for at least 7000 a. The people of these cultures, usually called Babylonians, developed a very sophisticated knowledge of mathematics and astronomy that is probably the oldest recorded science. Astronomical data gathered by the Babylonians is used by modern astronomers to expand their knowledge of the history of the universe.

Many other cultures also developed an early knowledge of astronomy. Some of these cultures were in regions of modern Egypt, China, India, and Central America. The Mayans in Central America developed extremely precise calendars.

One of the earliest methods of telling the time of day was by using a sundial. The time was indicated by the shadow cast on a specially marked surface. The sundial shown above is Chinese and dates back to the period of the Han Dynasty, 206 BC to AD 220.

Astronomical knowledge was essential to understanding seasons and in trying to predict natural events. The Chinese also developed a very precise seismograph that detected earthquakes. In a country that experiences many earthquakes, a seismograph was useful in identifying areas in need of emergency aid.

The numerous cultures that existed along the eastern end of the Mediterranean Sea from approximately 600 BC to AD 200 were essential to the development of science. The Greeks were noted for their geometry and the development of systematic thought. Because this area of the world was such a great trading centre, it also became a centre for the exchange of ideas. During this period, a great deal of knowledge about the world was collected and shared.

Science in the Arab cultures was stimulated by countless books and texts collected by Arab traders from around the world, starting in approximately AD 600. Arabic translations of these texts fed the curiosity of educated Arabs. They used the collected information to study mathematics and astronomy, investigate the human body, classify plants and animals, and study matter. Arabs were famous for their studies of the properties of substances. Many of the words used in chemistry come from Arab scholars, for example, alcohol, alkaline, and chemistry.

When the knowledge collected and expanded by the Arabs was translated into Latin, beginning in Spain in approximately the eleventh century AD, the groundwork was laid for what is now called the Scientific Revolution. Many scientists and historians feel that modern science was born in this period, from approximately AD 1500 to AD 1700.

Science began because of the curiosity of people in many cultures and was used to fulfil the needs of those societies. When communication developed between cultures, science grew more quickly.

Science is still carried out the same way today. With better communication around the world, science grows even more quickly and extends beyond cultural boundaries.

Connections

Presentation of Collected Specimens

No matter how well information is presented, it cannot compare with observing real objects or specimens. Displaying a collection or a specimen is the simplest way to show the real thing. These specimens should be materials that you have collected yourself. For example, a presentation on minerals should include rock specimens.

Live specimens require proper care. The use of live animals should be avoided. Check with your teacher or science fair supervisor about which animals, if any, can be used.

In a presentation of collected specimens, you should follow the advice given on page 263 for an information only presentation. Here are some other things you should do.

1. Carefully label specimens.
2. Arrange for their proper care.
3. Explain the role of the specimens in the exhibit.

Here are some things you should *not* do.
1. Use live animals unless permitted.
2. Clutter your exhibit of specimens.

A butterfly collection

A fossil collection

A stamp collection

Presentation of Working Models

The ideas that you discover in any investigation can usually be demonstrated. In some cases, you can build a working model. The ideas involved should be discussed in a written report included in your presentation.

Be careful of chemical demonstrations. Take adequate safety precautions and get approval from your teacher before working with chemicals.

In a presentation of a working model, you should follow the same advice as given on page 263 for an information only presentation. There are some other things you should do.

1. Choose a model or demonstration which is easy to explain.
2. Clearly explain the steps involved in the demonstration.

Here are some things you should *not* do.

1. Get someone else to build your model.
2. Expect the model to explain itself.

A student demonstrates how to make a square bubble.

Presentation of Experiments

Experiments are presented in the same way as other investigations. The set-up of the experiment should be demonstrated. If the whole experiment cannot be shown, samples can be provided.

A report on the experiment should be available. The table of results and the graphs produced should be produced on a large scale in an exhibit. If you are doing a presentation of an experiment, then you should consider the advice you have already read for the other four types of presentations.

9.6

Ideas for Independent Investigation

The following topics are only examples of the types of topics that would be suitable for you to attempt. They have been selected because they fit at least *three* of the following criteria.

1. They are familiar to students at your grade level.
2. They relate to topics in this book.
3. They are practical examples of science.
4. They are specific enough to research.

If none of the following topics appeals to you, choose one of your own. But make sure that your choice fits the criteria.

Topics suitable for experiments are labelled (E). Those suitable for model building are labelled (M).

General Category

1. Chapter 1
    Properties of Matter

2. Chapter 2
    Characteristics of Life

Topic Title

a) How to build a golf ball (E, M)
b) Graphite: The wonder material of sports equipment
c) Materials used in winter clothing (E)

a) A homemade microscope (M)
b) A comparison of microscopic life in two sources of water (E)

3. Chapter 3
Classification

a) How minerals are classified

b) How galaxies are classified (M)

4. Chapter 4
Classification of
Living Things

a) A dichotomous key to identify poisonous mushrooms

b) A dichotomous key for the birds of your province

5. Chapter 5
Physical Change

a) How does salt help keep roads snow free? (E)

b) How is distillation used in industry?

6. Chapter 6
Chemical Change

a) Common crystal structures (M)

b) The changes in the pH level of rain water or snow during one month (E)

c) How is steel made today and how was it made centuries ago?

7. Chapter 7
Using Energy

a) A model of an energy-efficient home (M)

b) A homemade solar cooker (E, M)

c) A comparison of the human eye and a TV camera (M)

8. Chapter 8
Plants in Your Life

a) Herbal remedies

b) The effect of nutrients on plant growth (E)

c) How to create artificial environments for plants (E)

Summary

Do you know how ants find food? Or how a stereo speaker works? It may not be important to know the answers to these particular questions. But it is important to be able to discover answers to questions that arouse your curiosity.

In this chapter, you have been given a plan for carrying out an independent investigation. You have also seen different ways to present the results of such an investigation.

Chapter Questions

Remember

1. What is a hypothesis?
2. Give three reasons for doing an experiment as part of an investigation.

Think

1. Why should you choose a topic that is already familiar to you?
2. After choosing your topic, you must choose a very specific question that you will try to answer. Why?
3. Why is it important to make a hypothesis at the beginning of your investigation?
4. Why is it important to control some conditions in your investigations?
5. Prepare a brief report on a Canadian scientist from the following list. If possible, include the same information asked for on page 255.
   a) Frederick Banting
   b) Charles Herbert Best
   c) J. Armand Bombardier
   d) John Polanyi
   e) Helen Hogg
   f) Gerhard Hertzberg
   g) Geraldine Kenney-Wallace
   h) Maud Menten
   i) Louis Siminovitch
   j) Wallace Rupert Turnbull
   k) J. Tuzo Wilson

Frederic Banting

Charles Best

J. Armand Bombardier

John Polanyi, Helen Hogg, and Gerhard Hertzberg

Geraldine Kenney-Wallace

Maud Menten

Louis Siminovitch

Wallace Rupert Turnbull

J. Tuzo Wilson

Dream

1. Scientists may make and test hypotheses about things that do not seem useful to society. Sometimes their only reason for doing research is to satisfy their own curiosity. Imagine a society where scientists always had to explain why their experiment was important to their society. What differences might there be between science in that society and science as you know it?

Decide

1. Consider a magician performing an illusion and a scientist doing an experiment. How are the purposes for their activities different? How are their skills different?

Glossary

Animals. Kingdom of living things that are mobile and have digestive and nervous systems.

Arm. The part of a microscope to which the barrel is attached

Barrel. A hollow cylinder to which the lenses of a microscope are attached

Biomass energy. Energy produced from recently dead plants and animals

Boiling. Process by which a liquid changes into a gas or vapor as a result of heating; sometimes used as a synonym for *vaporization*

Boiling point. Temperature at which boiling occurs

Cell. The basic unit of living matter of which all living things are composed

Cell membrane. Thin envelope of material surrounding the cytoplasm of a cell

Change of state. Physical change of a substance between solid, liquid, or vapor state

Chemical change. A change in which one or more substances disappear and are replaced with other substances

Chemical potential energy. Energy stored in fuels such as wood, oil, or gas

Chemical test. An examination of a substance to identify it or what it contains by how it reacts when combined with a test substance

Chemistry. The study of chemical changes

Chlorophyll. Green pigment in a plant necessary for photosynthesis

Chloroplastid. A cell body containing chlorophyll

Coarse adjustment. The large knob on a microscope used to move the barrel up or down by large amounts

Condensation. Process in which a gas or vapor changes to a liquid when cooled

Crystalline substance. A substance in which all pieces are made up of particles having the same size

Crystals. Particles of a substance that have flat sides and the same shape; e.g., salt, sugar

Cytoplasm. Watery fluid that makes up most of a cell

Dichotomous classification. A system of classification that divides information or objects into two sets until each set has only one member

Dichotomous key. Set of questions, usually *either/or* choices, used to divide things into sets in dichotomous classification

Dissolve. Particles of one substance intersperse among particles of another

Distillation. Process in which a liquid is heated and the vapor given off is collected and condensed

Elastic potential energy. Energy that is stored in anything that is stretched, compressed, or twisted out of shape yet will snap back to its original form

Electricity. A form of kinetic energy of charged particles, used to give light and heat, and to run machines

Elodea. A common water plant that grows in ponds, lakes, and aquariums

Energy conversion. Process when one form of energy is changed into one or more others

Energy converter. Object in which energy is converted; e.g., flashlight used to convert chemical energy into visible light + heat

Euglena. A microscopic organism found in pond water

Evaporation. Process in which a liquid changes to a gas or vapor at a temperature below its boiling point

Fair test. A test in which all of the conditions of the test are the same

Fibrous root. Root that branches out into the soil in all direction

Fine adjustment. The knob on a microscope used to move the barrel up or down by very small amounts

Fossil fuel. Substance that contains chemical energy produced by the sun's radiant energy in prehistoric plants

Fungi. Kingdom of plant-like living things that are not green and have no leaves

Gas. State of a substance that changes in shape and volume to fill a container

Geothermal energy. Heat energy produced inside the earth by several kinds of energy conversions

Germinate. To begin to grow; the start of growth in a seed

Germination. Growth of a seed when favorable conditions are present

Glucose. A product of photosynthesis; a form of sugar; an important energy source for living things

Gravitational potential energy. Energy stored in anything that is above the ground

Green plant. A plant that generally contains chloroplastids

Heat. A form of kinetic energy that, when added to matter, changes its state or temperature

Heating system. System that converts one of various forms of energy into heat energy

Hydroponics. Science of growing of plants in water, without soil, with nutrients added

Hypothesis. Possible explanation or solution of a problem, based on observations

Indicator. Special material used to show whether a substance is an acid or a base

Inference. An opinion or conclusion based on observations and knowledge from past experience

Iris diaphragm. A small, circular variable opening on a microscope used to control the amount of light passing upward through the hole in the stage

Irritability. Capacity of living things to react to changes in their environment

Isotherms. Lines on a map that connect areas of equal temperature

Joule. Unit used for measuring quantity of energy (*symbol*: J)

Kilogram. Basic unit for measuring mass (*symbol*: kg)

Kilowatt hour. Unit used to measure the amount of energy delivered at the rate of one kilowatt for one hour (*symbol*: kW·h)

Kinetic energy. Energy of moving particles, e.g., heat, sound, electricity

Lens paper. Special paper used to clean lenses on a microscope

Liquid. State of a substance that changes in shape to fit container but does not change in volume unless the temperature is changed

Litmus. An indicator used to determine whether a substance is an acid or a base

Malleable. Property of a substance that can be bent without breaking; e.g., metal

Mass. The quantity of matter in a given object

Melting. Physical change from a solid state to a liquid state

Melting point. Temperature of a substance at which melting or solidification occur

Metabolism. Process by which living things use energy

Microscope. An instrument with a combination of lenses for making small things look larger

Microscopic. Anything that is too small to be seen by the unaided eye

Monerans. Kingdom of microscopic living things that have no cell nucleus; e.g., bacteria

Neutralization. Name given to the reaction when bases and acids cancel each other's effects

Non-crystalline substances. Substances that are not made of crystals

Non-radiant energy. Energy possessed by objects

Non-renewable energy source. Source of energy that eventually will be used up

Nuclear potential energy. Energy stored in special fuels, such as uranium, that produce heat inside a nuclear reactor

Nucleus. A small, microscopic structure in a cell, usually round, and found near the middle of the cell

Objective lens. The lens at the lower end of the barrel on a microscope

Observation. Any property or behavior of objects or events that can be identified by one of your five senses or measured by devices

Ocular. The lens at the upper end of the barrel of a microscope; synonym for *eyepiece*

Organs. Major structures of a mature plant

Oxygen. A gas necessary for respiration in most living things

Phenolphthalein. Colorless solution used as an indicator to determine whether a substance is an acid or a base

Photosynthesis. Process by which certain living plant cells combine water with carbon dioxide in the presence of chlorophyll and light energy to form carbohydrates and release oxygen

pH scale. Quantitative scale used to measure strength of acids and bases

Physical change. A change in a substance in which properties are altered but no new substance is produced

Physical properties. Characteristics of matter that can be detected by using one or more of your five senses; e.g., shape, color

Plants. Kingdom of living things that are green and have leaves, stems, and roots

Potential energy. Energy that is stored in an object or system of objects

Power rating. Rate at which an appliance uses electricity

Primates. Group in the animal kingdom that includes all apes, monkeys, and humans

Problem-solving model. A systematic approach to solving a problem

Protists. Kingdom of microscopic, single-celled, living things that have a cell nucleus

Qualitative properties. Characteristics of a substance or object that can be described but not measured; e.g., smell or taste

Quantitative properties. Characteristics of a substance that can be measured or determined precisely

Radiant energy. Energy that behaves like light; e.g., radiowaves and television signals

React. Respond to a stimulus; e.g., irritability of a cell; combine with to produce new substances(s); e.g., a chemical reaction

Renewable energy source. Energy source that can be restored or renewed to add to the supply of energy

Reproduction. Process by which living organisms create other living things of their own kind

Solar energy. Radiant energy from the sun

Solid. State of a substance that does not change in shape or in volume unless the temperature is changed

Solidification. Physical change of state from a liquid to a solid

Solution. A solvent with one or more other substances dissolved in it

Solvent. A substance that can dissolve other substances

Sound. Sensation caused in the air by the vibration of the surrounding air

Specimen. The object that you observe when using a microscope

Stage. Flat structure on a microscope, supported by the arm, on which slides are placed

Starch. Substance produced when a plant converts excess glucose from photosynthesis for storage

States of matter. Forms in which all substances can exist: solid, liquid, or gaseous

Stoma. A small opening in a leaf through which transpiration takes place (*plural*: stomata)

Sublimation. Process in which a solid changes directly to a gas without first becoming a liquid; also the reverse change from a gas directly to a solid

Synthetic substance. Substance made from other substances in a laboratory

Tap root. Root consisting of one major, central part

Technology. The result of the application of science to solve problems in society

Thermostat. Instrument used to control a heating system at set temperature(s)

Transpiration. Process of water loss through a leaf

Vapor. State of a substance that changes in shape and volume to fill a container; sometimes used as a synonym for *gas*

Vaporization. Process by which a liquid changes into a gas or vapor as a result of heating; sometimes used as a synonym for *boiling*

Watts. A unit for measuring the rate of energy use, equivalent to joules per second (*symbol*: W)

Weight. A measure of the quantity of matter in a given object, which also depends on local gravity; sometimes used as a synonym for *mass*

Word equation. A statement used to represent a chemical change that takes place in matter

Index

Photograph Credits

Chapter 1: 2-3, Peter Paterson; 4, Symbion, Inc.; 5, LMP Athletic Locker; 10, 11 top, NASA; 11 bottom, U.S. Geological Survey; 14, E. Hayes/Miller Services; 16, United Church of Canada, Berkeley Studio; 18, HSMS/Sunnybrook Hospital; 20, © 1968, Yale University Library, New Haven, Connecticut, from *Alchemy and the Occult*, compiled by Ian Macphail with essays by R.P. Multhauf and Aniela Jaffé and additional notes by William McGuire; 22, Museum Boymans-van Beuningen, Rotterdam; 23, Larry Ostrom/Art Gallery of Ontario; 27, G.R. Beck/Public Archives Canada/PA-123055; 27, margin, University of Toronto Archives; 28, © Hystar 1985; 29, Historic Naval and Military Establishment, Penetanguishene, Ontario; 30, D. and J. Heaton/Miller Services; 31, top, Department of Fisheries and Oceans, Institute of Ocean Sciences; bottom, Ontario Ministry of Transportation and Communication.

Chapter 2: 32-33; From H.G. Wells, *The War of the Worlds*, The Bettman Archive; 34: D. Muench/Miller Services; 39; a), Ontario Hydro; b), Ontario Science Centre; c), HSMS/Sunnybrook Hospital, Toronto; 40, Ontario Centre of Forensic Sciences, Toronto; 41, lichen, Dr. Donald R. Gunn; aquarium, Ontario Science Centre; 43, Harry Turner/National Research Council; 44, Ron Dengler; 48, bottom, Ontario Science Centre; 49, HSMS/Sunnybrook Hospital; 50, Ron Dengler; 56, from *The Select Works of Antony Van Leeuwenhoek*, translated by Samuel Hoole, introduction by Frank N. Egerton, reprinted from a copy in The New York Academy of Medicine (New York: Arno Press, 1977), Harry Turner/National Research Council; 57, top, HSMS/Sunnybrook Hospital; bottom, Dr. F.P. Ottensmeyer/ University of Toronto; 58, Mexican Government Tourism Office; 59, Dr.

John Krug/University of Toronto; 60, Ontario Ministry of Agriculture and Food; 61, Ontario Ministry of Tourism and Recreation.

Chapter 3: 62-63, © Al Harvey/Masterfile; 64, 65, Peter Paterson; 67, margin, © J. Abecasis/Miller Services; 67, top right, Michael Saunders/Miller Services; 67, bottom, HSMS/Sunnybrook Hospital; 68, Ontario Geological Survey; 69, Miller Services; 75, United Church of Canada, Berkeley Studio; 76, HSMS/Sunnybrook Hospital; 77, top, Harry Turner/National Research Council; 77, bottom, U.S. Geological Survey; 78, Peter Paterson; 79, Harry Turner/National Research Council; 81, Atmospheric Environment Service; 84, 85, NASA.

Chapter 4: 86-87, Metro Toronto Zoo; 88, a), Minister of Supply and Services Canada; b), c), Ontario Science Centre; d), Ontario Ministry of Agriculture and Food; e), Metro Toronto Zoo; f), Dr. W.A. Crich, Royal Ontario Museum; 89, Ontario Science Centre; 90, Metropolitan Toronto Library Board; 91, a), Budd Watson/Miller Services; b), Ontario Ministry of Agriculture and Food; c), W. Griebling/Miller Services; 93, a), © Heather Angel; b), Ontario Science Centre; c), Ontario Ministry of Agriculture and Food; 94, Metro Toronto Zoo; 95, Ontario Science Centre; 96, Ontario Science Centre; 97, Harry Turner/National Research Council; 99, a), Connaught Laboratories Ltd., b), © Gene Cox and Jacques Berger; 100, c), Dr. Donald Gunn/Ontario Science Centre; d), Ontario Ministry of Agriculture and Food; e), Ontario Science Centre; 102, Metro Toronto Zoo; 104, © Lucasfilm Ltd., (LFL)1977, all rights reserved; bottom, Royal Ontario Museum; 105, Ontario Science Centre.

Chapter 5: 106-107, Cana-press; 108, left, Royal Ontario

Museum, Toronto; right, Geological Survey of Canada; 111, Ontario Science Centre; 113, General Motors Canada; 114, Peter Paterson; 117, Cominco Ltd.; 118, Agriculture Canada; 119, left, W. Free/Miller Services; right, Mark Tomalty/Masterfile; 120, Lynn McAfee/Miller Services; 121, a), Ontario Hydro; b), U.S. Geological Survey; c), United Church of Canada, Berkeley Studio; d), Newfoundland Department of Development and Tourism; e), Mike Dobel/Masterfile; 122, HSMS/Sunnybrook Hospital; 124, Atmospheric Environment Service, Communications Directorate; 125, Tony Stone/Masterfile; 128, Imperial Oil Limited; 130, margin, Public Archives of Canada/Imperial Oil Collection/PA-103280; bottom, Susan A. Cox; 131, Cliffs Dow Chemical Company/Flame-Glo Ltd.; 132, General Motors Canada; 133, M. Beedell/Miller Services; 134, Masterfile.

Chapter 6: 136-137, Peel Regional Police; 138, Peter Paterson; 139, Halifax Chronicle-Herald/Canapress; 140, Ontario Hydro; 142, a)–e), National Museum of Natural Sciences, f), Ontario Geological Survey; 143, Peter Paterson; 147, Ontario Ministry of the Environment; 150 top, Camerique/Miller Services; bottom, Peter Paterson; 154, Ontario Hydro; 155, Ontario Hydro; 157, Geological Survey of Canada; 159 a), United Church of Canada, Berkeley Studio; b), Ontario Hydro; c), Chuck O'Rear/Masterfile; d), Letki Designs; e), Peter Paterson; f), General Motors Canada; 160, The Royal Ontario Museum, Toronto; 161, coin, The Royal Ontario Museum; Toronto; 164, Mark Tomalty/Masterfile; 165, Institut de tourisme et d'hotellerie du Québec; 166, J.D. Taylor/Miller Services; 167, U.S. Geological Survey; 168, United Church of Canada, Berkeley Studio; 169, Ontario Research Foundation.

Chapter 7: 170-71,
© Wamboldt/Miller Services; 172, a),
Metro Toronto Zoo; b), Minolta
Canada; c), United Church of Canada,
Berkeley Studio; d), Ontario Hydro;
173, e), i), Metro Toronto Zoo; f),
General Motors of Canada; g), Harry
Turner/National Research Council;
h), j), Ontario Hydro; 174, margin,
United Church of Canada, Berkeley
Studio; bottom, Ontario Hydro; 175,
Ontario Hydro; 176, top margin,
Miller Services; bottom margin,
© A-J Verkaik; bottom, Canadian
Pacific; 177, 178, Trudi Le Caine,
Harry Turner/National Research
Council; 179, © Tony Stone
Worldwide/Masterfile; 180, Eldorado
Nuclear; 185, Ontario Ministry of
Agriculture and Food; 186, Bell
Northern Research Ltd.; 187, a),
Ontario Hydro; b), © Al
Harvey/Masterfile; c), Agriculture
Quebec; 191, United Church of
Canada, Berkeley Studio; 193,
Provincial Archives of Alberta; 194,
Ontario Hydro; 196, Scanada
Consultants Limited; 197, New
Balance Athletic Shoe, Inc.; 199,
Ontario Hydro; 201, Laurentian
University Library/Vincent Crichton
Collection; 204, top, H. Armstrong
Roberts; middle, © T. Bognar/Miller
Services; bottom, © Mark
Tomalty/Masterfile; 205, © Lynn
McAfee/Miller Services; 206, National
Research Council; 208, United
Church of Canada, Berkeley Studio;
209, Ontario Hydro.

Chapter 8: 210-11, F. Bruemmer;
212, I. MacNeil/Parks Canada; 213,
Miller Services; 215, Ontario Science
Centre; 218, Gordon Wick; 220, right,
Ontario Science Centre; left, © Ron
Watts/Masterfile; 221, top, United
Church of Canada, Berkeley Studio;
bottom left and right, Agriculture
Canada; 223, Gordon Wick; 225,
Ontario Ministry of Agriculture and
Food; 226, Ontario Hydro; 227, Inco
Limited; 230, a), b), Agriculture
Canada; e), Ontario Science Centre;
c), Ontario Ministry of Agriculture
and Food; d), Masterfile; f), Miller
Services; 231, Bill Whitman/Miller
Services; 232, Peter Paterson; 234,
Ontario Ministry of Agriculture and
Food; 235, Trevor Cole; 236, evening
primrose, Country Squire's Garden;
violets, James Hodgins; herbs,
© Mark Tomalty/Masterfile; 237, top,
Abitibi-Price Inc.; bottom, Ontario
Ministry of Agriculture and Food;
238, top, Ontario Ministry of
Agriculture and Food; 239, top, Peter
Paterson; bottom, Fisons
Corporation Limited; 240, Henry
Jones/Prince of Wales Northern
Heritage Centre, from *The Northern
Wild* by Marilyn Walker; 241, Royal
Ontario Museum, Toronto, *Study
Collection*; 242, Ontario Ministry of
Agriculture and Food; 244,
Newfoundland Department of
Development and Tourism; 245,
NASA.

Chapter 9: 246-47, Alberta
Government; 255, © Michael
Abbey/Science Source/Masterfile;
260, Yerkes Observatory/University
of Chicago; 262, Peter Paterson; 264,
Royal Ontario Museum, Toronto; 266,
stamps, Masterfile; butterflies, Harry
Turner/Agriculture Canada; fossils,
Ontario Geological Survey; 268,
Masterfile; 271, a), b), d), f), i),
University of Toronto Archives;
c), J. Armand Bombardier Museum;
e) University of Toronto
Communications; g), Instruction
Media Services, University of
Toronto; h), University of Toronto
Press.